| DATE DUE | | | |
|---|---|---|---|
| | | | |
| | | | |
| | | | |
| | | | |
| | | | |
| | | | |
| | | | |
| | | | |
| | | | |
| | | | |
| | | | |

GAYLORD M-2        PRINTED IN U.S.A.

# Recognition of Structural Pests and Their Damage

# Recognition of Structural Pests
# and Their Damage

Harvey L. Sweetman, Ph.D.

Professor of Entomology and Ecology
University of Massachusetts, Amherst

WM. C. BROWN COMPANY PUBLISHERS
135 SOUTH LOCUST STREET • DUBUQUE, IOWA 52003

Copyright © 1965
by
Harvey L. Sweetman

Library of Congress Catalog Number: 65-17546

*Manufactured by* WM. C. BROWN CO. INC., Dubuque, Iowa
Printed in U. S. A.

## WHY SHOULD PESTS BE IDENTIFIED

Identification is important for the householder, for the restauranteur, or other person, in charge of a structure or establishment, whatever its nature, for the pest control operator, or his service man, and for others who may wish to eliminate the pests. Identification informs you what the pest is, from which you can learn its habits, look for damage, locate additional infestation if present, and plan and execute a solution for the problem.

The key will assist you in identification of the common structural pests that attack us and our homes and structures and their contents such as foods, fabrics, furs, paper, wood and other materials therein. The pests themselves may be observed or collected for identification or signs such as hairs, fecal remains, tooth marks, foot prints, rub marks, cast skins, insect parts, etc., or the damaged products such as fabrics, furs, feathers, hides, paper, wood, foods and other materials usually have clues sufficient for determination of the causal pest.

The term "structural pest" refers to all pests that occur in any type of structure of man, or associated with the immediate environs of such structures. This automatically eliminates the thousandes of species of potential pests in habitats which never invade our structures except possibly by chance. Thus do not attempt to use this key for identification of insects or other organisms that are not structural pests, such as those which occur on outdoor plants, in soil, in forests, and are distant from structures. This key is intended only for those pests that normally invade our structures, except for a few general insects that are attracted to lights at night, and usually leave the structures as soon as the lights are cut off or daylight arrives. This latter type are not classified as structural pests.

### How to Use the Key

Who can use the key? Numerous students beginning their first study of insects and of structural pests have successfully used the key. Can you as a novice, householder, or inexperienced person, or a commercial pest control operator or his service man identify pests with this key? Yes, you usually can if you will apply these instructions.

The key is divided into a series of two-choice (dichotomous) couplets. Examine the pest specimen or specimens, evidences left by the pest, or the damaged materials, whichever you have, and read couplet 1 (left hand margin of page). Determine if the evidence fits the first or second half of the couplet. The next couplet to turn to is given on the right hand margin of the page. If the evidence you have fits the first half of couplet 1, the figure 2 on the right hand margin of the page directs you to couplet 2 (left hand margin); if the evidence fits the second half of the couplet, the figure 1010 on the right hand margin of the page directs you to couplet 1010 for further identification. You will always find on the right hand side of the page after each half of each couplet a number, a name, or a name and a number. If a name only, that is as far as you can identify the specimen or evidence; usually this is to species. If a number only is on the right hand side, turn to the couplet indicated and continue the two-choice selection. If a name and number are on the right hand margin, you have identified the evidence to a major group of the pest, but the number directs you on to another couplet for further identification.

When you have no idea what the pest is that is producing your problem, but have a possible pest, sign, or damaged material, always turn to couplet 1 and follow the above procedure to identification. If you have some idea what the pest is, for example you think it is an adult beetle (Coleoptera), look for the word "beetle" (common name) in the INDEX (or Coleoptera (taxonomic name) in the CONTENTS) and select the first major (underlined) figure, which is 379-549, and turn to couplet 379 and proceed with the two-choice identification. By knowing it was an adult beetle or coleopteron and starting with couplet 379, you have by-passed couplets 1, 2, 3, 4, 6, 177, 191, 192, 193 and 194. If you have a pest that you know is a fly, and suspect that it is a house fly, look for "house" under "fly" in the INDEX, which refers you to couplet 713. If it is a house fly, it should match the characters given in the first half of the couplet. If it does not, check against the last half of the couplet; if it still does not fit the characters, turn back to couplet 685, flies, and proceed to identify. Therefore when reasonably certain of the approximate identification of a pest, use the short-cut procedure; otherwise start with couplet 1.

It is essential to read both halves of each couplet carefully to determine which your evidence fits best. The specimen may have most, but not all, of the characters in either half of the couplet, still use the half of the couplet the evidence fits best and turn to the couplet number as directed for that portion of the couplet.

In using the INDEX look for the different kinds of pests under the group common name as ants, bees, birds, bugs, beetles, fleas, flies, moths, ticks, damaged materials, secondary signs, etc. For example, stink beetle would be given under "beetle, stink," or burn of a fabric would be under "damaged material, burn."

The identification key is profusely illustrated to assist you in determining the causal organism producing the damage or the pest itself. Use the illustrations associated with each respective couplet, or on occasion with an associated or nearby couplet when so directed. Be certain to read each portion of each couplet as well as the associated or referred to illustration. You will make far better progress if you read the couplet and observe the associated illustration, than by using either alone.

A few couplet numbers are omitted at intervals in the text. These spaces are intended for convenience of revision.

The cooperation and assistance of many people, including entomologists, students, pest control operators, householders, colleagues, and others have helped in one way or another during the development of this key over the years. Published works have been consulted freely.

Many illustrations are original, some have been taken from available sources, and many individuals, especially workers in the U. S. D. A., Rodent Control Branch of U. S. Fish and Wild Life Service, and U. S. Public Health have generously loaned others.

I am greatly indebted to all of those who have helped make this book more usable.

# AIDS IN IDENTIFICATION

A number of sources may be helpful as supplementary aids in identification. Regional keys, which limit the number of potential pests, will assist. The illustrated identification sheets prepared by the Communicable Disease Center and others can be helpful. Once the pest is identified general works on structural pests such as those of the National Pest Control Association and others should be consulted. A number of such readily available aids follow:

Anon. Pest control technology. Entomological section. National Pest Con-
  1950  trol Association, Inc. Elizabeth, N. J.
  1955  Stored grain pests. U. S. D. A., F. B. 1260.
  1961  Illustrated keys to the mosquitoes of the Tennessee Valley. Tenn.
        Valley Auth., Wilson Dam, Alabama.
  1961  Field manual on veterinary entomology for animal disease eradi-
        cation division personnel. Section on ticks. U. S. D. A., Anim.
        Dis. Erad. Div.

Baerg, W. J. The black widow and five other venomous spiders in the
  1959  United States. Ark. Agr. Exp. St. B. 608.

Baker, E. W., et al. A manual of parasitic mites. Nat. Pest. Control Ass.,
  1956  Elizabeth, N. J.

Beal, R. S. Jr. Synopsis of the economic species of *Trogoderma* occurring
  1956  in the United States with descriptions of a new species (Cole-
        optera, Dermestidae). Ann. Ent. Soc. Amer. 49,6: 559-66.
  1960  Description, biology and notes on the identification of some *Trogo-
        derma* larvae (Coleoptera, Dermestidae). U. S. D. A., T. B. 1228.

Burnett, D. Jr. Can you identify fabric pests? I-III. Pest Control 18,
  1950-51   11:9-11; 18,12:16-22; 19,1:16-20.

Carpenter, S. J. & W. J. LaCasse. Mosquitoes of North America. Univ.
  1955  Calif. Press, Berkeley, Calif.

Communicable Disease Center. Pictorial keys of structural pests. D. H.
        E. W., Comm. Dis. Center, Atlanta, Ga.
        Bats: pictorial key to United States genera.
        Pictorial key to some common beetles and weevils associated
        with stored foods.
        Pictorial key to some common adult cockroaches.
        Pictorial key to some common fleas in United States.
        Pictorial key to fleas found on domestic rats in southern United
        States.
        Taxonomic details of flies.
        Muscoid flies.
        Pictorial key to common domestic flies in southern United States.
        Pictorial key to mature larvae of some common flies.

Pictorial key to principal families of Diptera of public health importance.
Pictorial key to common domestic flies in southern United States.
Key characters of myiasis-producing fly larvae.
Lice commonly found on man.
Pictorial key to lice of domestic rats in southern United States.
Pictorial key to female mites commonly found on domestic rats in southern United States.
Differentiation of anophelines and culicines.
Pictorial key to some common mosquito larvae in western United States.
Pictorial key to United States genera of female mosquitoes.
Pictorial key to United States genera of mosquito larvae.
Pictorial key to anopheline larvae of United States.
Pictorial key to some common female mosquitoes of United States.
Field identificaton of domestic rats.
Pictorial key to genera of adult ticks in United States.
Pictorial key to some common ticks.

Gurney, A. B. Corrodentia (book lice). Nat. Pest Cont. Ass., Pest Cont.
1950    Tech.: 129-163.

Hughes, A. M. The mites of stored food. Brit. Min. Agr., Fish. & Food,
1961    T. B. 9:287 pp.

Jaques, H. E. How to know the insects. Wm. C. Brown Company, Du-
1947    buque, Iowa.

Kaston, B. J. & E. Kaston. How to know the spiders. Wm. C. Brown
1953    Company, Dubuque, Iowa.

Mallis, A. Handbook of pest control. MacNair-Dorland, New York.
1960

Pratt, H. D. & K. S. Littig. Ticks of public health importance and their
1962    control. Training Guide, Insect Control Series. D. H. E. W.,
        Comm. Dis. Center, Atlanta, Ga.

Rees, B. E. Classification of the Dermestidae (larder, hide and carpet
1943    beetles) based on larval characters, with a key to North Ameri-
        can genera. U. S. D. A., Mis. Pub. 511.

Smith, M. R. Key for identification of worker ants. Nat. Pest Con. Ass.,
1950    Pest Cont. Tech.: 259-300.

Snyder, T. E. Order Isoptera. The termites of the United States and Canada.
1954.   Nat. Pest Cont. Ass., T. B.

Stojanovich, C. J. Illustrated key to the common mosquitoes of northeastern
1961    North America. Emory Univ. Branch, Atlanta, Ga.

# CONTENTS

## TAXONOMIC DIRECTORY

### (See INDEX for common names)

# IDENTIFICATION OF STRUCTURAL PESTS

## A Key to the Arthropods (Insects and Their Allies), Vertebrates, and Other Animals Normally Occurring in and about Households and Other Structures of Man

1. Identification based largely on specimens of the pests, or animals, or cast skins of arthropods making the attack or producing the damage.                                                    2

   Identification based entirely on secondary evidences as damage, fecal remains, tooth marks, hairs, etc.                          1010

2. (1) Animals with segmented bodies, jointed appendages, and an exoskeleton; *or* their eggs, which lack the segmented bodies and jointed appendages.

   Phylum ARTHROPODA      3

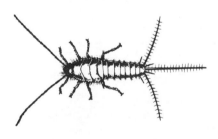 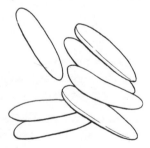

   Animals with a backbone (endoskeleton); *or*, if lacking an endoskeleton, active stages lack body segmentation, jointed appendages, or exoskeleton, although the body may be covered with a hard calcareous shell.

   ANIMALS other than ARTHROPODA      31

3. (2) Adults, or immature stages (nymphs) resembling adults in form; active: walk (crawl, run) or fly, or both.    4

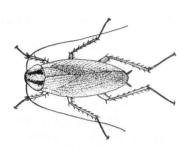 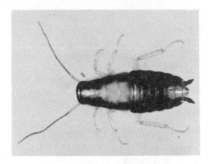

Immature stages; inactive (eggs, egg capsules, most pupae), *or,* active stages (larvae, caterpillars, maggots, grubs, mosquito pupae, etc.) but not resembling adults in form.

IMMATURE INSECTS    830

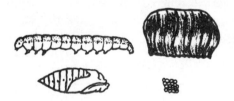

4. (3) Legs numerous, exceeding 10 pairs; body long and slender.    5
   Legs, or leglike appendages, fewer, not exceeding 10   pairs.    6

5. (4) Antennae relatively long and slender, many segments, 12 or more; a single pair of legs on most body segments behind head, the first pair often modified into poison claws; body usually flattened; opening to reproductive organs near hind end of body; largely carnivorous.

Centipedes, hundred legged worms, order CHILOPODA    8

Antennae relatively short, about 7 segments; 2 pairs of legs on each segment behind the fourth; lacking poison claws; body usually cylindrical and firm; opening to reproductive organs near front of body; usually roll into ball when disturbed; largely herbivorous.

Millipedes, thousand legged worms, order DIPLOPODA    12

6. (4) Adults with 3 pairs of thoracic legs; 1 pair of antennae; 3 body divisions (head, thorax, and abdomen).

Insects, class INSECTA or HEXAPODA    177

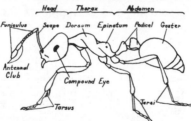

Typically 4 or more pairs of legs; if less than 4 pairs, the antennae lacking; 1 or 2 body divisions.        7

7. (6) Five or more pairs of legs, or leg-like appendages; 2 pairs of antennae, 1 minute, the other readily visible.

Amphipods, sowbugs, and pillbugs, class CRUSTACEA    21

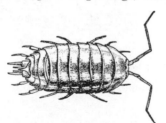

Usually 4 pairs of legs, occasionally less (newly hatched mites and ticks may have only 3 pairs of legs); antennae lacking. Spiders, ticks, mites, scorpions, pseudoscorpions, whip scorpions, and harvestman or daddy-long-legs,

class ARACHNIDA    23

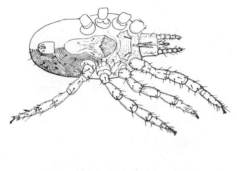

## CHILOPODA (Centipedes)

8. (5) Fifteen pairs of legs.                                  9

    Twenty or more pairs of legs, legs not longer than 2-3 times the body width; antennae and last pair of legs much shorter than length of body.                           10

9. (8) Legs much longer than width of body, the last pair much elongated; antennae and last pair of legs longer than body; 8 dorsal plates; length up to 32 mm. or more. Widespread, common in structures.

House centipede, Scutigera cleoptrata et al.

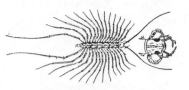

    Legs shorter; 15 leg bearing segments.
Family LITHOBIIDAE: Lithobius spp. et al.

10. (8) Twenty-one to 23 pairs of legs; with or without eyes (illust. 11). Occasionally invade structures.
Family SCOLOPENDRIDAE     11

    Thirty-one or more pairs of legs; lacking eyes. Rarely invade structures.

Family GEOPHILIDAE

11. (10) Eyes (4 ocelli) present; length up to several inches.
Genus Scolopendra: S. heros, S. morsitans,<br>S. polymorpha et al

Eyes lacking, or only 1 ocellus.

Genera *Otocryptops, Theatops, Cryptops*

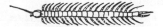

## DIPLOPODA (Millipedes)

12. (5) Integument soft; cannot roll into a ball or spiral.

Family POLYXENIDAE: genus *Polyxenus*

Integument hard; usually capable of rolling into a ball or spiral.                     13

13. (12) Mouthparts suctorial.

Family POLYZONIIDAE:
genera, *Polyzonium, Platydesmus*

Mouthparts chewing.                     14

14. (13) Nineteen to 21 body segments, somewhat flattened.

Family POLYDESMIDAE     15

More than 25 body segments; cylindrical.                     16

15. (14) A spine on lower side of base of each leg. Occasionally invade structures.

Genus *Fontaria*:
*F. virginica* et al.

Spine lacking.                     Other genera

16. (14) Twenty-six to 30 segments; anal segment ending in 2 papillae. Rarely invade structures.

Family CRASPEDOSOMIDAE

Usually more than 30 segments; anal segment curved or ending in a spine.                     17

17. (16) Sternites (ventral plates) after the seventh free from pleurites (dorsal plates); only the first pair of legs on seventh segment of male copulatory.

Family CALLIPODIDAE: genus *Callipus*

Sternites after the seventh usually fused with pleurites; both pairs of legs of seventh segment of male copulatory. Occasionally invade structures.

Family JULIDAE    18

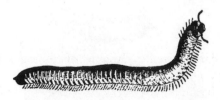

18. (17) Legs of seventh segment of male modified for mating, readily visible; eyes with 40 to 60 ocelli (facets); last segment more or less prolonged into a spine. Occasionally invade structures.

Genera *Parajulus* et al.:
P. *impressus*, P. *venustus* et al.

Mating legs of seventh segment hidden. Occasionally invade structures.

(Genus *Julus*)    19

19. (18) Thirty to 35 body segments; yellowish with a dark mid-dorsal line.

Genus *Brachyiulus*

Thirty-five to 60 body segments.    20

20. (19) Thirty-five to 42 body segments.

Genus *Diploiulus*

Forty-nine to 60 body segments.

Genus *Ophyiulus*

## CRUSTACEA

21. (7) Body flattened from sides; some of ventral body appendages not resembling legs; hinder legs used for jumping; brown-

ish-black; up to 13 mm. Damp locations, occasionally invade structures. Western and southern.

Order AMPHIPODA: amphipods,
*Talitrus sylvaticus*

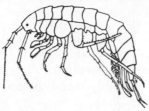

Body flattened dorso-ventrally (from above to below); all legs, 7 pairs, very much alike; do not jump, (illust. 22). Occasionally invade basements and damp locations.

Isopods, order ISOPODA    22

22. (21) Two tail-like appendages shorter than antennae; can roll into loose ball when disturbed; length up to 16 mm.

Sowbugs, family ONISCIDAE: genera *Porcellio*,
*Oniscus* et al.

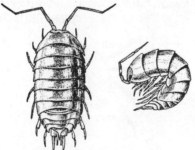

Lacking 2 tail-like appendages; can roll into tight ball when disturbed; length up to 16 mm.

Pillbugs, family ARMADILLIDIIDAE:
genus *Armadillidium* et al.

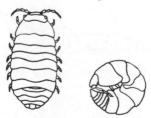

## ARACHNIDA

23. (7) Body ovoid, or nearly so, except small forms less than 3 mm. long, then body may be elongated; cephalothorax (head

and thorax) unsegmented; cephalothorax and abdomen not distinct; usually 4 pairs of legs, occasionally less (illust. 24, 25).

MITES, TICKS, and HARVESTMAN    24

Body not ovoid, usually in 2 divisions, cephalothorax (head and thorax) and abdomen distinct; segmentation more or less distinct; 4 pairs of legs (illust. 26).    26

24. (23) Legs very long and slender, many times the length of body, 4 pairs; abdomen segmented.

HARVESTMAN or daddy-long-legs, order PHALANGIDA

Legs short or only moderately long; abdomen not segmented (illust. 25).

Mites and ticks, order ACARINA    25

25. (24) Usually larger, more than 1 mm. up to 13 mm. when engorged; leathery cuticle; beak (hypostome) provided with strong, recurved teeth; attack man and other mammals.

Ticks, suborder IXODIDES    93

Smaller, usually less than 3 mm., often minute usually soft, some hard-shelled (sclerotized). Parasites, scavengers, or in foods.

MITES    120

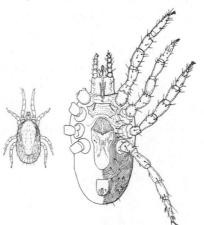

26. (23) Two distinct body divisions, the legs attached to the first; second division (abdomen) joined to cephalothorax by a slender waist; body segmentation more or less distinct. Free-living webmakers.

Spiders, order ARANEIDA    155

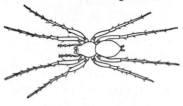

Not as above.    27


27. (26) Elongate, the tail-like abdomen robust and bearing on its end a poison stinger; first pair of legs shorter than rest. Largely Southwest and South.

Scorpions, order SCORPIONIDA:
*Centruroides vittatus* et al.

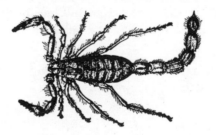

Not as above.    28


28. (27) First pair of legs much elongated; whiplike or threadlike tail without sting; Cephalothorax separated from abdomen by a constriction. Non-poisonous.

Vinegarroon, whip scorpions,
order PEDIPALPIDA

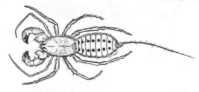

Not as above.    29

29. (28) Head distinct from thorax, with very large, pinching structures; thorax 3 segmented.

Solpugids, order SOLPUGIDA

Crab-like, tiny, usually less than 10 mm., flattened forms, with relatively huge chelicerae.

Pseudoscorpions,
order PSEUDOSCORPIONIDA: *Chelifer cancroides* et al.

31. (2) Animals lacking a backbone; body soft, sometimes covered with a shell; a pair of conspicuous tentacles usually bearing eyes near the tip; move by gliding on a mucus film (these shiny films on surfaces are good evidence of activity of snails and slugs) (illust. 32). Occasionally invade basements and other damp areas in structures. Snails and slugs, phylum MOLLUSCA.                                                                    32

Animals with a backbone; outer covering of feathers, hair, scales, or a smooth or rough skin.                                            33

## MOLLUSCA (Slugs and Snails)

32. (31) Carrying a calcareous shell into which the body can be withdrawn. Active at night or in damp situations. Feed on vegetation and organic matter as paper and other items when damp.                                                                          SNAILS

Lacking a shell. Habits similar to snails, but in wetter habitats.                                                                        SLUGS

33. (31) Body covering of skin or scales; lacking hair or feathers.    34
Skin, except very young, covered with hair or feathers; never
scaled, except legs of birds.    44

34. (33) Body covered with smooth or warty skin, moist; lack
scales; 4 legs (illust. 35).

Salamanders, frogs, and toads,<br>class AMPHIBIA    35

Skin covered with scales, usually dry; with or without legs
(illust. 36).

Snakes and lizards,<br>class REPTILIA    36

## AMPHIBIA (Frogs and Toads)

35. (34) Tailless; skin smooth or warty, more or less moist; active
at night, in damp situations, or in rain. Rarely invade structures except under damp conditions; often fall into window
wells, and enter basements through open doors, windows, or
other openings. Feed on arthropods and other small animals.
Harmless to man.

FROGS and TOADS

With tails; skin smooth and moist; active at night, especially when moist and wet. Rarely invade structures, but may
fall into window wells and enter basement as do frogs and
toads. Feed on arthropods and other small animals. Harmless to man.

SALAMANDERS

36. (34) With 4 legs; with few exceptions; usually in dry situations; active during daylight, often at night. Largely feed on arthropods and other small animals.

LIZARD    37

Lacking visible legs; long and slender.

SNAKES    39

37. (36) With beadlike tubercles scattered over body; mottled black and yellow or reddish; up to 24 inches or more. Feed on insects, small animals, bird's eggs, etc. Poisonous, dangerous to man. Rarely invade structures. Utah and Southwest.

Gila monster, *Heloderma suspectum*

Lacking beadlike tubercles and color as above.    38

38. (37) Color changeable from dull brown to vivid green; tail longer than head and body. Often invade structures for insect food; tame. Harmless to man. North Carolina to Texas.

American chameleon, *Anolis carolinensis*

Lack above combination of characters, but similar in appearance and shape. Largely insect feeders. Harmless to man.

Other LIZARDS

39. (36) Eyes with vertical or cat-like pupils; a deep dimple or pit on side of head halfway between eyes and nostril; a pair of hollow poison fangs on roof of mouth. Poisonous, very hazardous to man. Occasionally enter structures, usually barns or more open buildings. Feed on rodents, small birds, frogs, toads, etc.

Pit vipers, family CROTALIDAE  40

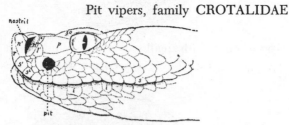

Lacking pit between eye and nostril. 43

40. (39) No rattles on tail. 41
    Rattles on end of tail.

RATTLESNAKES 42

41. (40) Back brownish, cross bars of reddish brown widening on side to hour-glass shape; belly whitish, a row of dark spots on each side. Massachusetts to Texas.

Copperhead, *Agkistrodon mokosen*

Back brownish, cross bars narrow; belly yellow, with dark blotches.

Water moccasin, *Agkistrodon piscivorus*

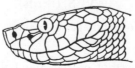

42. (40) Top of head with large plates arranged symmetrically (alike).

Pigmy rattlesnakes, *Sistrurus* spp.

Top of head with small scales, mostly unsymmetrical (unlike).
Larger rattlesnakes, Crotalus spp.

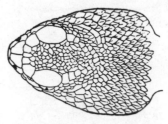

43. (39) Body completely ringed with yellow, red, and black, the red and yellow rings adjoining. Small and nocturnal; poison is hazardous. Feed on arthropods and other small animals. Southern.

Coral snakes, family ELAPHIDAE:
*Micrurus fulvius, Micruroides euryxanthus*

Body not so colored and patterned. Feed on insects and rodents, some often entering and living in barns and loose buildings. Harmless to man, usually beneficial.
Numerous NON-POISONOUS SNAKES

44. (33) Body covered with feathers.

Birds, class AVES  45

Body covered with hair.   Mammals, class MAMMALIA  52

## AVES (Birds)

45. (44) Pests because of damage to wood, drumming on wood or metal, or pecking windows.  46

Pests because of nesting or roosting habits.  47

46. (45) Pecking on windows by fighting reflection in glass.
Any ground-inhabiting MALE BIRD

Drilling in wood or drumming on loose boards or metal.
Woodpeckers, sapsuckers, and flickers, family PICIDAE

47. (45) Nest in chimneys. Often infested with chimney swift bed bug, which rarely enters structures or bites man.
Chimney swift, *Chaetura pelagica*

Nesting elsewhere. Structures may become infested with mites, and occasionally bedbugs, that develop on the birds. Accumulation of droppings may attract flies, produce odors and become unsightly.                                48

48. (47) Build mud nests under eaves, in attics, or in barns.
Barn swallow, *Hirundo rustica erythrogaster*,
Cliff swallow, *Petrochelidon pyrrhonota*

Nests of other types and materials.                            49

49. (48) Nest in bird boxes, holes in trees, and similar places.
Tree swallow, *Iridoproche bicolor;* purple martin, *Progne
subis subis*, starling, *Sturnus vulgaris vulgaris*, house
sparrow, *Passer domesticus domesticus*, few song birds
Nest on ledges, in attics, crevices, or in vines and bushes.   50

50. (49) Nest in vines and bushes.
House sparrow, *Passer domesticus domesticus;*
robin, *Turdus migratorius;* other song birds

Nest on ledges, in attics, and crevices.                       51

51. (50) Nest on wide ledges, attics, wall spaces, and similar situations.
Pigeons, *Columba livia;* starlings, *Sturnus vulgaris vulgaris;*
House sparrow, *Passer domesticus domesticus*

Nest on narrow ledges.
Robins, *Turdus migratorius*,
phoebes, *Sayornis phoebe* et al.

# MAMMALS

52. (44, 1071) Fingers on each fore limb greatly elongated and supporting a leathery membranous wing; flying mammals. Often roost in belfries, attics, wall spaces, under eaves, etc. More often observed flying about in the evening at twilight, feeding on flying insects. Generally beneficial. Rabid bats occasionally attack man—see a doctor.

BATS, order CHIROPTERA

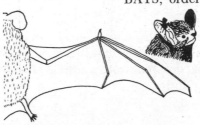

Feet with claws, fingers not elongated to support a membranous wing.                                                                53

53. (52) Front teeth (incisors) smaller than canine teeth.        54

Incisor teeth larger than others, or about equal in size to others.                                                                57

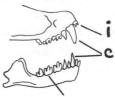

54. (53) Small mammals with definitely black and clear white variable color pattern; tail long and hairy, lacking definite color rings; 5 toes on hind feet; claws not retractile (illust. 55, 56). Feed on vegetable and animal matter. Often live under porches, under houses, and may invade basements.

Skunks, family MUSTELIDAE        55

Small mammals, not as above.

Various carnivores, order CARNIVORA

55. (54) One or 2 white stripes lengthwise of body (illust. 56).    56
    White blotches or spots (stripes interrupted); smaller than
    above.

Spotted skunks, genus *Spilogale*

56. (55) White spot on head typically forking to form 2 white
    stripes on each side of body. Widespread.

Striped skunks, genus *Mephitis*

A broad dorsal white stripe from  head to tail. Along Mexican border.

Hog-nosed skunk, genus *Conepatus*

57. (53) Incisors and canines not much different from other teeth
    (illust. 58 also); snout long and pointed, with upper lip pro-
    jecting beyond the lower; not much more than 10 inches long.

Moles and shrews, order INSECTIVORA    58

Incisor teeth larger than others; canines absent leaving a gap
between incisors and back teeth.  Gnawing mammals.

Rodents, hares, rabbits, order RODENTIA    59

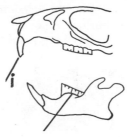

58. (57) Front feet very large and wide; lacking external ears; length including tail 5-10 inches. Burrow in soil. Feed on plants and small animals, especially insects and earthworms. Yard pests, produce ridges and mounds.

MOLES, family TALPIDAE

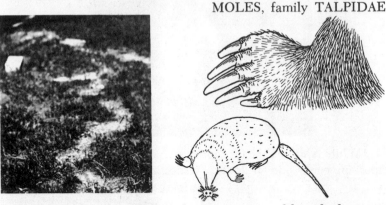

Front feet not so developed; ears present, although they may be almost hidden in fur; usually less than 5 inches; resemble mice, but with a much more pointed snout. Feed on animal matter, alive or dead on and below soil surface. Yard pests to a limited extent.

SHREWS, family SORICIDAE

59. (57) Two very small incisor teeth behind the pair of large upper incisors; tail short; hind legs considerably longer than front legs (illust. 60).

Hares and rabbits, family LEPORIDAE    60

Lacking the small upper incisor teeth.    64

60. (59) Ears usually less than 4 inches long, not black tipped, but often with  blackish tinge towards tip; tail white beneath, longer than wide; body more than 12 inches long; hind feet less than 4 inches long; fur not becoming white in winter. Yard pests, feeding on bushes, especially in winter.

Cottontail rabbits, genus *Sylvilagus*    61

Ears more than 4 inches long; ears and hind legs noticeably long (longer than domestic rabbits and cottontails). Not structural pests.

HARES, genus *Lepus*

61. (60) Tops of hind feet usually white; South Dakota and Oklahoma westward.      62

    Tops of hind feet usually buffy; Wyoming and Colorado eastward.      63

62. (61) Ear, from crotch, less than two and three-eighths inches long.

Rocky mountain cottontail, *Sylvilagus nuttallii*

Western cottontail, *Sylvilagus audubonii*

Ear slightly longer in adult.

63. (61) Under parts pinkish buff, well streaked with black; limited to east of Alleghenies. Maine and Vermont to Virginia.
New England cottontail, *Silvilagus transitionalis*

Under parts sprinkled, not streaked with black; largely New York west to Wyoming and Colorado.
Common cottontail, *Silvilagus floridanus*

64. (59) Body bristling with large, stiff quills. Sometimes gnaw on structures, especially around doors and windows.

PORCUPINES, Family ERETHIZONTIDAE

Lack quills; tail evident. 65

65. (64) Four or more grinding (cheek) teeth on each side of jaw. 66

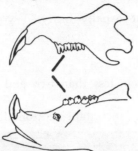

Only 3 grinding (cheek) teeth on each side of each jaw. 79

66. (65) Tail bushy, or at least well covered with hair.

Chipmunks, squirrels, woodchucks, family SCIURIDAE 67
Tail thinly haired, or almost bare. 78

67. (66) Body very heavy set; tail short, less than one-fourth of body length, without conspicuous black or white tip; thumb small, with flat nail; upper parts reddish brown (illust. 68). Occasional yard pests.

WOODCHUCKS or MARMOTS 68

Body more slender, tail usually, but not always longer. 69

68. (67) Under parts buff to brown. Eastern, west to Dakotas, Nebraska and Kansas.

Marmot, groundhog or woodchuck, *Marmota monax*

Under parts yellowish to light brown. Rockies and westward.

Yellow-bellied woodchuck, *Marmota flaviventris*

69. (67) With definite lengthwise stripes on back and sides.     70

Lacking definite color stripes.     72

70. (69) Upper parts with about 5 dark stripes, stripes on cheeks. Occasionally yard pests (illust. 71).

CHIPMUNKS     71

Stripes not as above. Rarely structural pests (illust. 69, 74).

GROUND SQUIRRELS

71. (70) Mid-dorsal stripe bordered on each side by a wider band; 4 upper grinding teeth on each side. Dakotas eastward. Usually lives in ground or in rock walls or crevices.

Eastern chipmunk, *Tamias striatus*

Mid-dorsal stripe bordered on each side by a lighter stripe of about equal width; 5 upper grinding teeth on each side. Dakotas westward.

Western chipmunks, genus *Eutamias*

72. (69) Front and hind legs on each side joined together by a wide fold of skin extending from side of body (illust. 73). May build nests in attics, wall spaces, and in bird boxes.

FLYING SQUIRREL    73

Lacking the wide fold of skin.    74

73. (72) Under parts white to roots of hairs; length with tail less than 10 inches. Eastern and central states.

Eastern flying squirrel, *Glaucomys volans*

Under parts with hairs dark at base; usually over 10 inches long. Northern and western states.

Northern or western flying squirrel, *Glaucomys sabrinus*

74. (72) Length of tail, minus hair, about one-third of total length; hairs with winding streaks of black, live in ground (illust. 69 also). Rarely structural pests.

GROUND SQUIRRELS

Tail about as long as head and body, bushy; live in trees (illust. 75, 76). Sometimes structural nuisances.

TREE SQUIRRELS    75

75. (74, 1074) Four grinding teeth in each side of jaw; color rusty to blackish, hairs on tail tipped with yellow, not white; length with tail 20-27 inches. Central states into East.

Fox squirrel, Sciurus niger

Five grinding teeth in each side of upper jaw, the first very small, sometimes absent; reddish or gray.          76

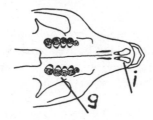

76. (75, 1074) Small, length with tail usually 14 inches or less; rusty-red above, white or rusty below. Forested areas east of Rockies.

Red squirrels: Sciurus hudsonicus et al.

Large, 17-20 inches; grayish above.          77

77. (76) Wooded areas from Atlantic Coast to Minnesota and Louisiana.

Eastern gray squirrel, *Sciurus carolinensis*

West Coast; tail very broad, with hairs often 3 inches long.
Western gray squirrel, *Sciurus griseus*

78. (66) Fur-lined cheek pouches on each side of mouth, but not connecting with mouth; thick-bodied with very short legs; fore feet much enlarged for digging; eyes and ears very small. Burrowing mammals. Central, western and southern states. Lawn and garden pests.

Family GEOMYIDAE: pocket gophers, west, *Thomomys* spp., east, *Geomys* spp.

Lacking fur-lined cheek pouches; tail a little shorter or longer or about the length of head and body.          79

79. (65, 78, 1041, 1072) Grinding teeth of upper jaw with rounded points in 3 lengthwise rows on the crowns; tail practically hairless, with fine scales. Old World rats and mice. Important structural pests.

Family MURIDAE          80

Grinding teeth with rounded points extending lengthwise in 2 rows, or with flattened crowns showing loops or irregular, triangular folds of enamel. More pestiferous in isolated structures.

Native rats and mice, family CRICETIDAE    82

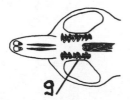 

80. (79) Total length from nose to tail up to 6-7 inches.
House mouse, *Mus musculus*

Total length up to 15-17 inches.

RATS    81

81. (80, 1075) Length from nose to base of tail greater, sometimes equal to, length of tail; grayish or brownish above, shading to lighter below. Worst structural rat pest.
Norway or house rat, *Rattus norvegicus*

Length from nose to tail less than length of tail, reddish brown to black above, yellowish white to slaty gray below.
Roof rat, *Rattus rattus rattus*

82. (79) Rounded points on grinding teeth extending in 2 lengthwise rows; tail usually hairy.

Rice rat, *Oryzomys* spp.,
mice as *Peromyscus* spp. et al.

Grinding teeth with flattened crowns showing loops or irregular triangular folds of enamel.

Cotton rats, *Sigmodon* spp.,
wood rats, *Neotoma* spp.,
many native MICE

**IXODIDES (Ticks)**

93. (25) Scutum (dorsal shield) lacking; mouthparts (capitulum)
ventral in nymphs and adults; integument leathery and peb-
bled, or spiny. Soft ticks.

Family ARGASIDAE 94

Scutum present, but sometimes small; capitulum anterior and visible from a dorsal view; integument smooth. Hard ticks.

Family IXODIDAE    104

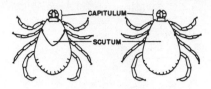

94. (93) Margin of body thin and acute; sutural line separating dorsal and ventral surfaces.

Genus *Argas*    95

Margin of body rounded; sutural line always lacking.    97

95. (94) Body nearly circular, flat (discoidal).

Bat tick, *Argas vespertilionis*

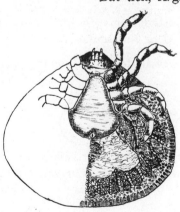

Body not circular, longer than broad.    96

96. (95) Margin of body striate (parallel fine lines), rounded in front; dorsum (upper surface) with fine wrinkles and discs. Engorge rapidly. Western states. Cliff swallows, wild birds.

Swallow tick, *Argas cooleyi (reflexus)*

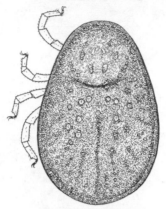

Margin of body not striate; dorsum with distinct quadrangular discs. Engorge rapidly. Southern states. Fowls and wild birds.

Fowl tick, *Argas persicus*

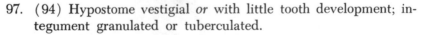

97. (94) Hypostome vestigial *or* with little tooth development; integument granulated or tuberculated.　　　　98

Hypostome with well developed teeth, never scoop-like on

dorsal surface; integument (illust. 100) mammillated (nipple-like processes), lacking spines. On various mammals.

Genus *Ornithodorus*　　99

98. (97) Nymphs (the stage usually seen) with integument spinose; hypostome well developed; adults with integument granular; hypostome vestigial (reduced). Common on horses, cattle, rabbits, man. Southwestern United States.

Genus *Otobius*: ear tick, *O. megnini*

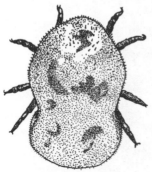 

Integument of adults and nymphs tuberculated; hypostome of adult scoop-like. Associated with bats.

Genus *Antricola*

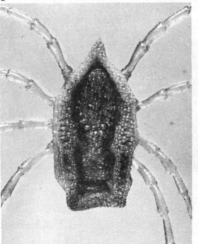

99. (97) Cheeks or flaps at sides of emargination between head and body; tarsi lacking humps, fourth tarsi lacking long subapical protuberance.    100

Cheeks absent.    101

100. (99) Discs rounded, large and easily seen. Southern United States.

*Ornithodorus talaje*

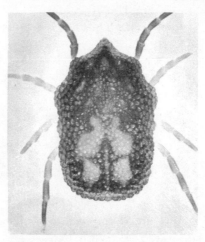

Disc very small and inconspicuous. Tropical.

*Ornithodorus rudis*

101. (99) Eyes present, the anterior eyes much larger than posterior eyes; fourth tarsi with spurs. California to Mexico.

*Ornithodorus coriaceus*

Eyes lacking. 102

102. (101) Dorsal humps lacking on all tarsi. Bird and mammal nests, man. Western United States.

*Ornithodorus hermsi*

Dorsal humps on some tarsi; fourth tarsi lacking dorsal humps and subapical protuberance.    103

103.  (102) Mammillae (tubercles) large, relatively few, not crowded; first tarsi with 3 humps above. Rodents, hogs, man. Southern United States and Mexico.

Relapsing fever tick, *Ornithodorus turicata*

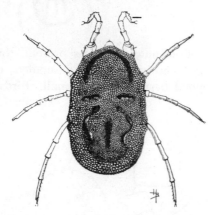

Mammillae small, crowded and numerous. Rodents, man. Western United States.

*Ornithodorus parkeri*

104.  (93) Eyes lacking.    105

Eyes on margin of scutum; anal groove behind anus (illust.

105), indistinct or absent.

105. (104) Anal groove in front of anus; festoons (rectangular areas divided by distinct grooves along posterior margins) absent. Worldwide. Rodents, carnivores, birds, man.

Genus *Ixodes*

Anal groove behind anus; festoons present, though less apparent in engorged specimens; second segment of palpi projects laterally beyond basis capituli. Small. Birds and rabbits.

Genus *Haemaphysalis*

 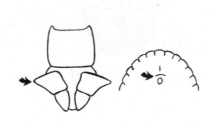  

106. (104) Palpi long, second segment twice as long as wide; hypostome with denticles largely restricted to spical (end) half. Tropical to subtropical.

Genus *Amblyomma*     107

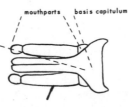

mouthparts    basis capitulum

Mouthparts short, second segment of palpi about as long as wide.

108

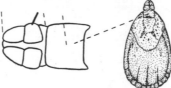

107. (106) Next to last tarsal segment of second, third and fourth legs lacking paired terminal spurs; female with distinct pale markings near hind end of dorsal shield (scutum); first coxa of male with internal spur moderately long; 2 pale horseshoe marks at end of abdomen. Central Texas to Atlantic Coast, north to Iowa. Birds, mammals: dog, man.

Lone star tick, *Amblyomma americanum*

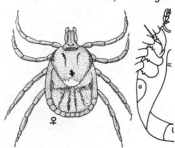

Next to last tarsal segment of second, third and fourth pairs of legs with long, paired terminal spurs; female with more diffuse marking on dorsal shield; first coxae of male with internal spur very small or absent. Southern United States. Birds, mammals: dog, man.

Gulf coast tick, *Amblyomma maculatum*

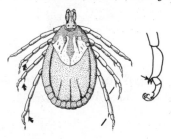

108. (106) Basis capituli laterally produced.                     109

Basis capituli not laterally produced.                     110

109. (108) Anal groove distinct, posterior to anus; festoons present; fore coxae deeply cleft; palpi not ridged; ventral shields (back of hind legs) present in males, absent in females. Worldwide. Mammals: dogs, occasionally man.

Brown dog tick, *Rhipicephalus sanguineus*

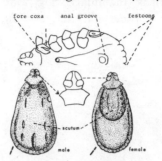

Anal grooves lacking; festoons lacking; fore coxae not deeply cleft; palpi ridged dorsally and laterally. Deer, livestock.

Cattle tick, *Boophilus annulatus*

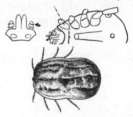

110. (108) Festoons 11; hypostome with denticles (teeth) always in 6 rows, 3 on each side and occupying most of its length. Worldwide.

Genus *Dermacentor* 111

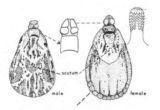 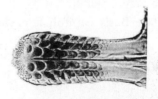 

Festoons 7; hypostome with denticles in 8 rows, 4 on each side, spurs (illust. 107 lower) on hind coxae short or absent. Tropical America, southern Texas and Florida.

Tropical horse tick, *Anocentor* (*Dermacentor*) *nitens*

111. (110) Genital opening visible on under side.

ADULTS   112

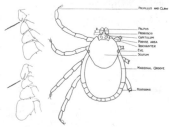

Genital opening lacking.

NYMPHS   116

112. (111) Spurs on first coxa widely divergent (spreading); scutum with deep, large punctures (pits).

*Dermacentor parumapterus*

Spurs on first coxa with proximal edges parallel, or nearly so.   113

113. (112) Spiracular (respiratory) plate oval, lacking or little dorsal prolongation, goblets (round structures in spiracular plate) few and large. Widespread. Domestic and wild animals, man. Scutum conspicuously marked with white.

Winter tick, *Dermacentor albipictus*

Scutum lacking white or with little white.

Brown winter tick, *Dermacentor nigrolineatus*

3          4

Spiracular plate oval, with dorsal prolongation often prominent; goblets small, many to moderate in number.   114

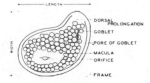

114. (113) Posterior lateral extensions of basis capituli long. Pacific Coast. Livestock, wild mammals.

Pacific Coast tick, *Dermacentor occidentalis*

Posterior lateral extensions of basis capituli moderate in length. 115

115. (114) Spiracular plate with goblets very numerous and small. East and Southwest. Mammals: dog, man.

American dog tick, *Dermacentor variabilis*

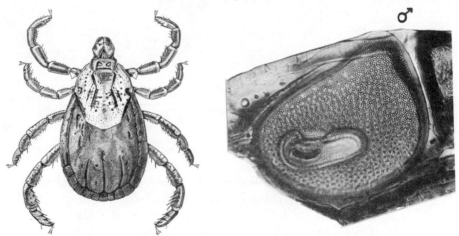

Spiracular plate with goblets moderate in size and number; large punctures of scutum (dorsal shield) very large and deep. Western states south to northern Arizona and New Mexico. Mammals: livestock, man.

Rocky Mountain wood tick,
*Dermacentor andersoni* (*venustus*)

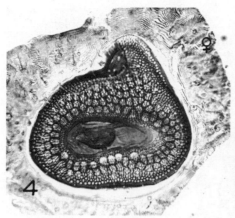
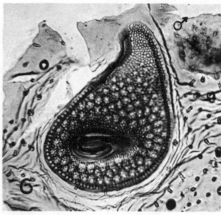

116. (111) Spurs lacking on fourth coxa.    117

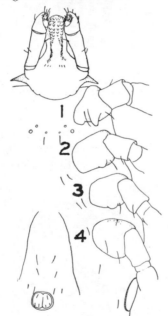

One external spur on fourth coxa (illust. 111).    118

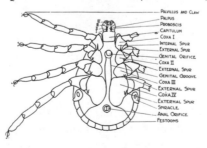

PALVILLUS AND CLAW
PALPUS
PROBOSCIS
CAPITULUM
COXA I
INTERNAL SPUR
EXTERNAL SPUR
GENITAL ORIFICE
COXA II
EXTERNAL SPUR
GENITAL GROOVE
COXA III
EXTERNAL SPUR
COXA IV
EXTERNAL SPUR
SPIRACLE
ANAL ORIFICE
FESTOONS

117. (116) Spiracular plate elliptical with very numerous goblets; spiracular opening eccentric (off center) (illust. 115 also). Mammals: dog, man. East and Southwest.

American dog tick, *Dermacentor variabilis*

Spiracular plate ovoid, distinctly broader at lower end, with few goblets; spiracular opening in broader end. Pacific Coast.

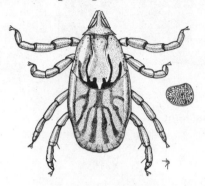

Mammals: rodents, livestock.

Pacific coast tick, *Dermacentor occidentalis*

118. (116) Spiracular plate large, circular; goblets about 10 in number. Widespread. Mammals: livestock, man.

Winter tick, *Dermacentor albipictus*

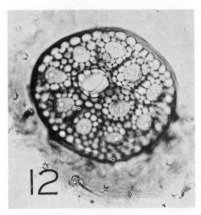

Spiracular plate circular or nearly so (subcircular); goblets numerous and small (illust. 119).                                                    119

119. (118) Spiracular plate subcircular, the spiracular opening not centered (subcenter). Western states, south to northern Arizona and New Mexico. Mammals: livestock, man.

Rocky mountain wood tick,
*Dermacentor andersoni* (*venustus*)

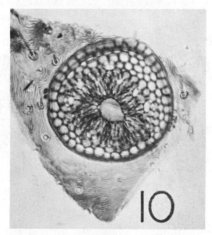

Spiracular plate short, oval, the spiracular opening eccentric in broad end.

*Dermacentor parumapterus*

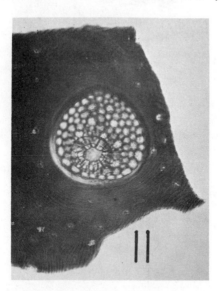

## ACARINA (Mites)

The major groups of structural pest mites are given in couplets 120-125, which lead into couplet 126. Couplets 126-154 are based largely on mite habitat. Turn directly to couplet 126, if the habitat or host of the mites is known.

120.  (25) Pedipalpal (foot-like palpus) tarsus with 1 or 2 simple or tined claws, pedipalpal coxae fused dorsally so that gnathosomal base forms a tube enclosing the mouthparts. Not likely to be structural pests.

Suborder MESOSTIGMATA (in part)

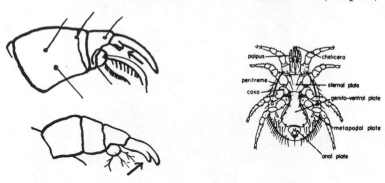

Pedipalps without tarsal claws, or with a single tined claw on inner proximal margin of tarsus.                                       121

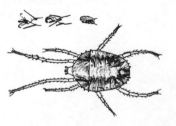

121.  (120) Body wormlike, annulate (ringed); 2 or 4 pairs of legs (illust. 122).

Suborder Trombidiformes (in part)    122

Body not wormlike or annulate; 1 to 4 pairs of legs (illust. 123).                                                                      123

122.  (121) Two pairs of anteriorly placed legs; plant feeders.
Family ERIOPHYIDAE: ERIOPHYID MITES    132

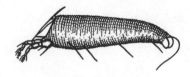

Four pairs of legs. In hair follicles.
Family DEMODICIDAE: FOLLICLE MITES 132

123. (121) One pair of stigmata (breathing pores), lateral on body in area between coxae II and anterior margins of coxae IV; usually 1 mm. or less in length.

Suborder MESOSTIGMATA (in part):
Families DERMANYSSIDAE, LAELAPTIDAE 126

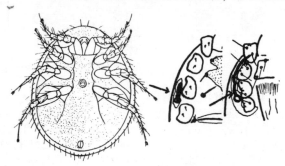

Not as above. 124

124. (123) Usually well sclerotized (hard-shelled) anal and genital plates well developed and without suckers.

Suborder SARCOPTIFORMES (in part):
ORBATID MITES 126

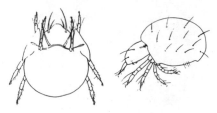

Not as above. 125

125. (124) Clawlike empodium arising from membranous pretarsus, *or* empodium a stalked suckerlike organ on more than 1 pair of legs; without true claws.

Suborder SARCOPTIFORMES (in part): cheese, flour, food, and furniture mites, families ACARIDAE and GLYCYPHA-GIDAE; parasitic mites on man and rodents, families SAR-COPTIDAE, PSOROPTIDAE, and LISTROPHORIDAE    126

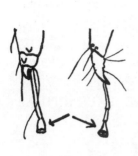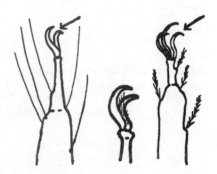

Not as above.

Suborder TROMBIDIFORMES (in part): harvest and itch mites, family PYEMOTIDAE; clover mites, family TETRA-NYCHIDAE; fowl and rodent mites, families CHEYLETI-DAE, MYOBIIDAE; roach mite, family PTERYGOSOMIDAE; chigger mites, family TROMBICULIDAE; bright red mites on soil, family TROMBIDIIDAE    126

126. (123, 124, 125) Small to large, very active, bright red to scarlet, usually on soil. Occasional individuals may enter structures. Normally not structural pests, but may stain light colored surfaces when mashed; do not attack man, attack arthropods.

Family TROMBIDIIDAE

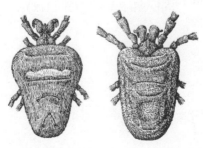

Not as above.    127

127. (126) Dullish green to dark brown or reddish, indoors crawling on window sills, walls, or floors, and furniture; when numerous, on basement walls and windows and outdoors on foundations and walls when warm. Do not attack man, but may stain objects when crushed.                    128

Color and habits not as above.                    129

128. (127) Largely around windows and on walls indoors or foundations and above outdoors; active on warm fall, winter and spring days. May cover walls, floors, and furniture when numerous.

Family TETRANYCHIDAE: clover mite complex; *Bryobia praetiosa* et al., brown wheat mite, *Petrobia latens*.

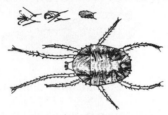

Crawling on furniture and desks in homes, especially in areas near roach colonies. Rarely or never seen running about in great abundance. Certain evidence of roach infestation.
Family PTERYGOSOMIDAE: cockroach mite,
*Pimeliaphilus podapolipophagus*

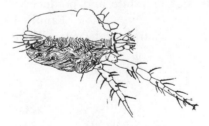

129. (127) Hard-shelled (heavily sclerotized), resembling minute beetles. Feed on fungi and organic matter.
Suborder SARCOPTIFORMES (in part): ORBATID MITES

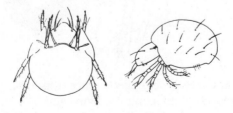

Not hard-shelled.                    130

130. (129) Elongate, often wormlike, annulate (ringed). 131

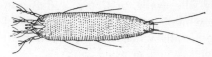

More or less oval to elliptical in shape (illust. 134). 134

131. (130) Tiny, very long and wormlike. On plants, man and
domestic vertebrate animals. 132

Elongate, not wormlike; broader than above, 2-3 times as
long as broad. 133

132. (122, 131) Two pairs of legs, placed anteriorly, infest plants,
produce whitish to chlorotic condition of leaves (illust. 130).
Family ERIOPHYTIDAE: ERIOPHYID MITES

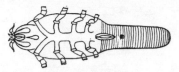

Four pairs of legs; infest man and domestic vertebrate animals. In hair follicles.
Family DEMODICIDAE: FOLLICLE MITES

133. (131) Elongate, 8-legged, with a wide space between the
first 2 pairs of legs and the last pairs of legs; length about 3
times the width, except gravid females, which may be greatly
distended behind the last pair of legs. Associated with grain
infesting insects, but may bite and produce irritation to man.
Family PYEMOTIDAE:
straw itch mite, *Pyemotes ventricosus*

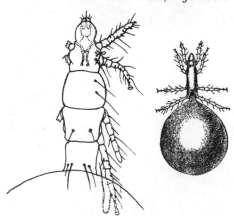

Elongate, apparently 6-legged, since the first pair of legs
are greatly modified to cling to hairs and are hardly recognizable as legs; length about 2 times the width. Rats and mice.
Family MYOBIIDAE: MYOBIID MITES 142

134. (130) Infesting foods (cheeses, dried fruits, cereals and cereal products). May produce itch or dermatitis on man.

Families ACARIDAE: grain mite, *Acarus siro* et al.; GLYCYPHAGIDAE: *Glycyphagus domesticus* et al.

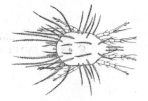 

Not infesting foods.                                                        135

135. (134) Infesting birds and fowls, or associated with nesting and roosting sites.                                            136

Not associated with birds and fowls.                            139

136. (135) Attacking legs of birds and fowls, becoming imbedded beneath the scales and produce swollen and deformed feet and legs, sometimes on comb and neck. Very debilitating.

Family SARCOPTIDAE:
scaly leg mites, *Knemidokoptes mutans* et al.

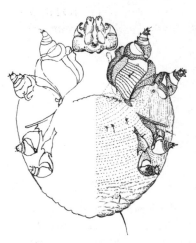 

Very active, producing symptoms different from above; not imbedded. May be very debilitating. Chicken mite, northern fowl mite, tropical fowl mite, bird and bird nest mites.

Family DERMANYSSIDAE       137

137. (136) Dorsal plate broad, not divided, tapering to rounded point behind, setae on plate smaller than surrounding setae; ventral plate narrow, tapering to a rounded point; anal plate forming an ellipse (egg-shaped), narrowest behind. Warmer regions. Largely replaces *Ornithonyssus sylviarum* (illust. 138) in South. Fowls and birds, attacks man.

Tropical fowl mite, *Ornithonyssus bursa*

Dorsal plate much broader behind.                          138

138. (137) Dorsal plate broad, not divided, tapering gradually behind into a broad truncate (very broadly rounded) end; ventral plate broad, tapering behind slightly to a broadly rounded tip; anal plate broad and square on front side. Cosmopolitan. Birds and fowls, attacks man.

Chicken mite, *Dermanyssus gallinae*

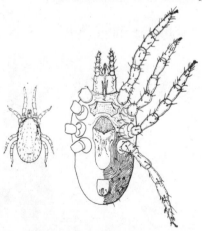

Dorsal plate not divided, broad and rounded for first three-fourths, the back fourth tapering very slightly to a very broadly rounded end; ventral shield broad in front, tapering to a narrowly rounded point behind; anal shield similar to ventral shield; feathers around anus matted with eggs. Temperate regions. Largely replaces *Ornithonyssus bursa* (illust. 137) in North.

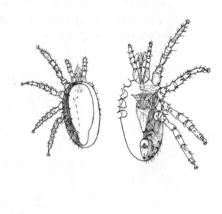

Northern fowl mite, *Ornithonyssus sylviarum*

139. (135) Usually associated with rats and mice; free-living on rodents.

Families DERMANYSSIDAE, LAELAPTIDAE,
LISTROPHORIDAE et al.    140

Associated with man and other mammals, including rodents; burrow into skin for feeding purposes.

LAELAPTIDAE, LISTROPHORIDAE et al.    152

140.  (139) First and second pairs of legs widely separated from third and fourth pairs of legs; the hind pairs may be more closely spaced on some Listrophoridae, but never closely approximated.    141

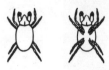

All 4 pairs of legs closely approximated.    144

141.  (140) Third and fourth legs of female, third legs of male, modified for clasping hairs; tip of abdomen with a pair of setae nearly half as long (male) to more than half as long (female) as body. Mice, guinea pig and other rodents.
Family, LISTROPHORIDAE: myocoptic mange mite,
*Myocoptes musculinus*

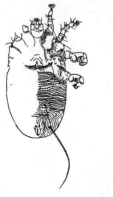

Legs not modified for clasping hairs.    142

142.  (133, 141) Palpi small, inconspicuous, without pectinate (extended on 1 side) setae; tip of abdomen with 2 long setae (illust. 143 also). Mice.

Family MYOBIIDAE    143

Palpi large, conspicuous, with 2 pectinate setae; tip of abdomen lacking 2 long setae.

　　Family, CHEYLETIDAE: lung mite, *Cheyletus eruditis*

143. (142) Second tarsus with 2 claws.　　　　*Radfordia ensifer*

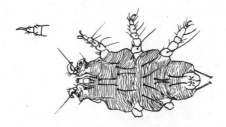

　　　Second tarsus with 1 claw.　　　　*Myobia musculi*

144. (140) Dorsal shield small, centrally located, not covering entire dorsum; genito-ventral plate narrow, tapering behind fourth coxae.　　　　　　　　　　　　　　　　　145

　　　Dorsal shield large, nearly covering dorsum; genito-ventral plate expanded behind fourth coxae.　　　　　　　146

145. (144) Dorsal shield divided into large anterior and small posterior plates. Commonly on mice but attack rats, occasionally man.

Family DERMANYSSIDAE: house mouse mite.
*Allodermanyssus sanguineus*

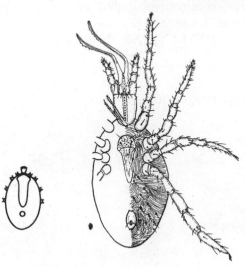

Dorsal shield not divided. Commonly on rats, produces irritation and dermatitis on man.

Family DERMANYSSIDAE: tropical rat mite,
*Ornithonyssus bacoti*

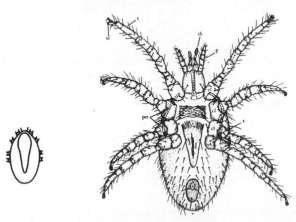

146. (144) Fore tarsus with claws and caruncle.                           147
Fore tarsus without claws and caruncle.

Family MACROCHELIDAE: house fly mite,
*Macrocheles muscaedomesticae*

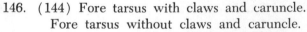

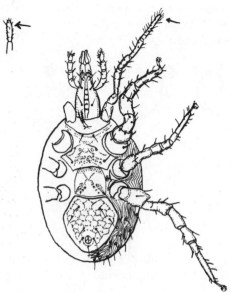

147. (146) Fore legs inserted with mouthparts into same body opening of host. Largely associated with earthworms.

Family UROPODIDAE: earthworm mite,
*Fuscuropoda agitans*

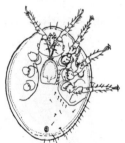

Fore legs not inserted with mouthparts in same opening of host.

Family LAELAPTIDAE 148

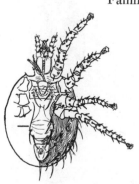

148. (147) Metapodal (between legs) plates behind fourth coxae
small; anal plate longer than wide; dorsal setae normal, not
enlarged toward end.                                                149

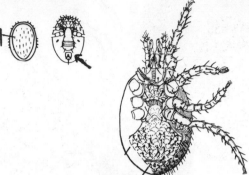

Metapodal plates behind fourth coxae large; anal plate
wider than long. On rodents, etc.

*Eulaelaps stabularis*

149. (148) Genito-ventral plate with 1 pair of setae; all coxae
lacking spurs.                                                      150

Genito-ventral plate with 4 pairs of setae; first 3 pairs of
coxae with spurs.                                                   151

150. (149) Femur and tibia of second leg normal, lacking stout
spines.

Common rodent mite, *Haemolaelaps glasgowi*

Femur and tibia of second leg each with a stout spine.

*Androlaelaps setosus*

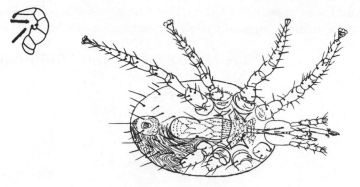

151. (149) Genito-ventral plate concave posteriorly; anal plate fitting into concavity.

Spiny rat mite, *Echinolaelaps echidninus*

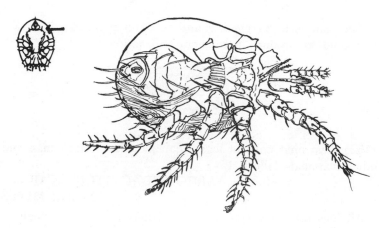

Genito-ventral plate convex posteriorly; widely separated from anal plate.

Domestic rat mite, *Laelaps nuttali*

152. (139) Tiny, 6-legged, red, burrow into skin for feeding; usually crawl onto man from grass, shrubs and bushes; commonly attack in areas restricted by close fitting clothing. Produce intense itching, especially after scratching; areas heal in 1-2 weeks.

Family TROMBICULIDAE: CHIGGERS

Tiny, sluggish, 8-legged, round in outline; burrow into skin and tend to produce permanent infestations.                        153

153. (152) Two hind pairs of legs inconspicuous. Attack man and other mammals (illust. 154).

Family SARCOPTIDAE: ITCH, SCAB and
MANGE MITES        154

All legs relatively conspicuous. Attack domestic animals.

Family PSOROPTIDAE: scab and mange mites, genera *Psoroptes* (p) and *Chorioptes* (c)

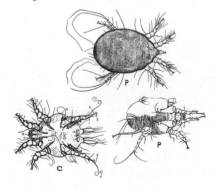

154. (153) On man and larger mammals.

Itch mite, *Sarcoptes scabiei*

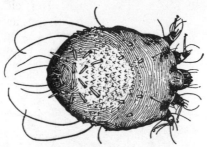

On cats, dogs, rabbits, rats and other rodents. Does not attack man.

Mange mite, *Notoderes cati*

## ARANEIDA (Spiders)

155. (26) Chelicerae projecting forward horizontally and with the fang articulated (joined) so as to be movable in a plane more or less parallel to median plane of body; 2 pairs of lungs (L); abdomen lacking tergites (dorsal plates); anal tubercles (A) immediately behind spinnerets; furrow of chelicerae distinct; tarsi with 2 claws and with claw tufts (illust. 159); body length 30-40 mm. or more. Large hairy spiders; poison minor. More common in West and South.

Family THERAPHOSIDAE: tarantulas, genus *Eurypelma* et al.

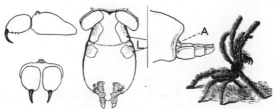

Chelicerae projecting downward and with fangs articulated (joined) so as to move in a more or less transverse plane; with 2 pairs of lungs, *or* 1 pair of lungs and a single median

tracheal spiracle, (S), *or* a pair of spiracles between lung slits
(L) and base of anterior spinnerets; lacking a cribellum (C)
and calalmistrum (CA). 156

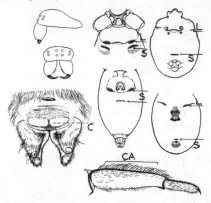

156. (155) Chelicerae fused at base, each provided at end (distally) with a lamella drawn out to a tooth, which with the
fangs, forms a kind of chela (pincer). 157

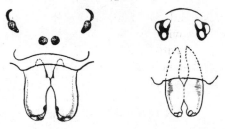

   Chelicerae not fused at base and lacking a lamella; 8 eyes. 159

157. (156) Tarsi (T) long and flexible, with many false segments;
spiracle lacking; labium (lower lip) broader than long. Webs
sheet-like, in cellars and dark sites, the spiders hanging in an
inverted position beneath web.

       Family PHOLCIDAE: long-legged spiders,
             genus *Pholcus* et al.

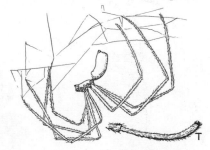

   Tarsi of usual type, with 2 claws and lacking false segments;
spiracles (S) spaced from spinnerets at least one-sixth the distance to epigastric furrow (E); 6 eyes, in 3 groups of 2 each,

the middle 2 far forward of others; carapace appreciably more than two-thirds wider than long, flat; sternum much wider than long, pointed behind; thoracic furrow (F) conspicuous and longitudinal. Irregular web. Live under stones and bark and in caves; common in structures.

Family LOXOSCELIDAE: FALSE HACKLED BAND SPIDERS    158

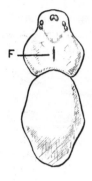 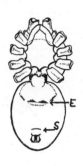

158. (157) Medium sized, body about 9.5 mm. long and 4.7 mm. wide, light brown with a thin coat of light brown hairs; legs long, dark brown with blackish hairs. Very poisonous, producing an extended necrosis about wound. Common in structures. Missouri, Arkansas, Texas, etc.

*Loxosceles reclusa*

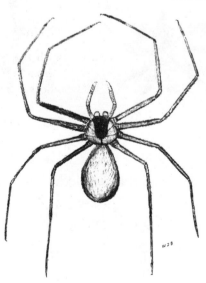

Similar to above; closely related. Presumably poisonous.
CLOSELY RELATED SPIDERS

159. (156) Tarsi with 2 claws, with or lacking claw tufts (t) (if tufts are present it can be safely assumed there are 2 claws). 160

Tarsi with 3 claws, never with tufts, but spurious claws. may be present; spinnerets in usual arrangement, not in a transverse row; eye group not hexagonal (6-sided). 165

160. (159) Eyes in 3 rows, the first row with 4 eyes, the medians the largest, the second row of 2 very small, often minute eyes, the third row with 2 median-sized eyes.

Family SALTICIDAE, jumping spiders, genus *Phidippus* et al.

 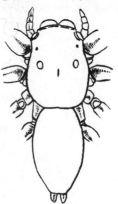

Eyes in 2 rows; tracheal spiracle just in front of spinnerets. 161

161. (160) At least legs I and II turned so that the dorsal surface is posterior and prolateral (nearest front side on inside) surface appears to be dorsal.                                  164

Legs of the usual prograde type; anterior spinnerets (S) touching or almost so, and not more heavily sclerotized (hardened) than the posterior spinnerets; eyes alike. Common in litter and under stones; tubular webs in rolled leaves.

Family CLUBIONIDAE     162

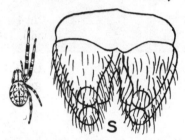

162. (161) Endites (E) lacking a depression; leg I longer than leg IV; cephalothorax light yellow to greenish, brownish at most only in eye region; legs of same color; sternum not distinctly margined; eyes about equal in size, the hind medians nearer to each other than to the hind laterals; thoracic groove lacking.

Genus *Chiracanthium*     163

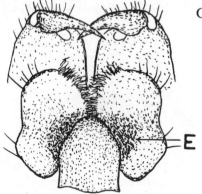

Lacking the combination of characters above.
Family CLUBIONIDAE: other GENERA

163. (162) Color pale yellow to pale green, the cephalothorax darker, chelicerae dark brown; female 8-9 mm., male 6 mm. Common in structures. Poison produces severe pain for few hours. Widespread.

*Chiracanthium inclusum*

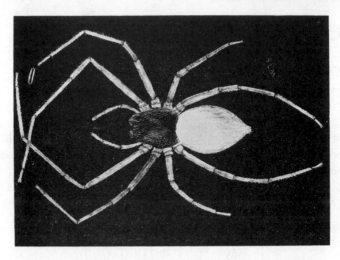

Cephalothorax and legs yellowish brown, the legs paler, abdomen pale yellowish brown with faint shading of green; female about 9.5 mm. long. Common in structures. Hawaii.

*Chiracanthium diversum*

164. (161) Colulus (C) absent; retromargin (margin of fang furrow below or behind the fang) of cheliceral fang with teeth; apex of metatarsus with a soft trilobate membrane, allowing hyperextension of tarsus. Largely in warmer regions.

Family SPARASSIDAE: giant crab spiders, genus *Heteropoda* et al.

Colulus present; chelicerae with retromargin of fang furrow smooth; the inner (promargin) margin alone with at most 1 or 2 teeth; apex of metatarsus sclerotized (hardened) so that hyperextension of tarsus is impossible.

Family THOMISIDAE: crab spiders, genus *Thanatus* et al.

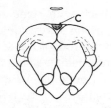

165. (159) Tarsus IV, for at least one-sixth of its length from distal end, with a ventral row of 6-10 curved serrated bristles forming a comb. Spiders hang in an inverted position in irregular webs.

Family THERIDIIDAE    166

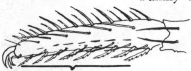

   Tarsus IV lacking such a comb; tarsi with a single row of trichobothria, which increase toward the distal end; trochanters not notched. Live in web tunnels, over which they run in upright position.

Family AGELENIDAE: genus *Tegenaria* et al.

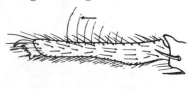

166. (165) Dorsal and epigastric scuta lacking; lateral eyes on each side at least a diameter of one eye apart; abdomen globose, usually dark to black with red, or red and white spots.

Genus *Latrodectus*    167

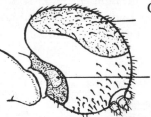

   Scuta absent as above; lateral eyes on each side less than a radius of one apart.

Genera *Steatoda, Theridion* et al.

167.  (166) Black with some red spots, typically a dark red hour glass figure on lower side of abdomen; male and young females usually with row of red spots above, flanked on each side with white lines; female about 12 mm. long, abdomen globose, 7.5-9 mm. wide, male 3.6-4.2 mm. long. Widespread, commonly·invade structures.  Very poisonous.

Black widow spider, *Latrodectus mactans*

Brown, less black, or more gorgeously colored.  Southern.      168

168.  (167) Light gray to light brown, sometimes almost black, hourglass figure on under side of abdomen brownish-yellow, pattern above as illustrated, variable; female about 9.5 mm. long, male 3.2 mm.  Invade structures.  Less poisonous than black widow.

Brown widow spider, *Latrodectus geometricus*

Cephalothorax and legs often bright orange color, sometimes yellow, sometimes brick red; abdomen above with variously

shaped carmine spots, the front ones edged with yellow; hour-
glass spot under abdomen not resembling an hour glass, half
yellow and half reddish-orange. Not common in structures.
Not very poisonous. Southern half of Florida.

Red-legged widow spider, *Latrodectus bishopi*

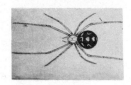

## HEXAPODA (Insects)

177. (6) Wingless forms, or with wings reduced to mere stubs
(wing pads) as with most nymphs.                                   178

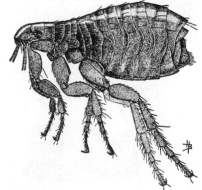

With wings, either 2 or 4 (the elytra or wing covers of
beetles are the front wings).                                      191

178. (177) Swiftly running insects of small size, the abdomen ending in 3 tails; body covered with flattened tiny scales.
Order THYSANURA: SILVERFISH, FIREBRAT    206

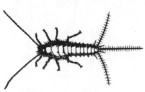

Body lacking tails; not covered with flattened tiny scales.    179

179. (178) Ectoparasites on birds and mammals; body not flattened laterally (from sides); antennae set in pits and not visible from above; ticklike.

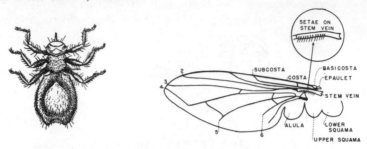

       Order DIPTERA: wingless BLOOD-SUCKING FLIES    685
    Not as above.    180

180. (179) Small, delicate, with 6 or less abdominal segments; usually with furculum or spring (ventral abdominal appendage) on posterior ventral abdomen, used for leaping; antennae shorter than body, with few segments. Length up to 6 mm.

       Order COLLEMBOLA: SPRINGTAILS    199

    Not as above; furculum always lacking.    181

181. (180) Sucking mouthparts.    182

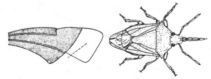

    Chewing mouthparts.    184

182. (181) Body strongly compressed (flattened from sides); spines on body directed backward; hind legs for jumping; 5 tarsal segments. Associated with pets, rodents, fowls.

Order SIPHONAPTERA: FLEAS    655

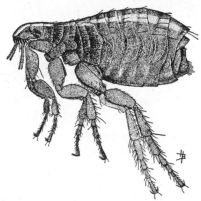

Not as above.    183

183. (182) Fleshy unsegmented beak, usually retracted, showing a slit surrounded by stout sucker hooks; tarsi of legs ending in a single claw that is opposable to a terminal spur on tibia for grasping hairs, etc. Man and other mammals.

Order ANOPLURA: SUCKING LICE    280

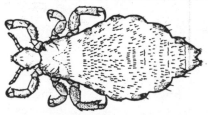

Beak segmented, slender, arising at front end of head and extending between legs, except when feeding; tarsi of legs with 2 claws.

Order HEMIPTERA: TRUE BUGS    342

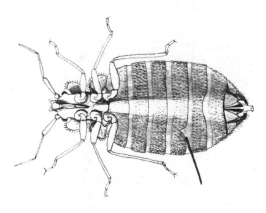

184. (181) Abdomen ending in a pair of movable pincers or forceps.

Order DERMAPTERA: EARWIGS    256

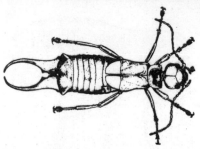

Lacking forceps.    185

185. (184) Body strongly constricted or threadwaisted between thorax and abdomen, with 1 or 2 swellings or knobs on pedicel, knobs occasionally lacking on pedicel; antennae usually elbowed. Small to large in size. True ants, occasionally antlike wasps.

Order HYMENOPTERA: ANTS    587

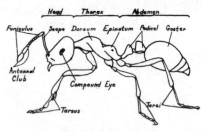

Body not threadwaisted, base of abdomen as broad as thorax, or nearly so; antennae not usually elbowed.    186

186. (185) Yellowish brown to black, except abdominal intersegmental membranes; white or brownish wing stubs on thorax remaining after long wings were broken off.

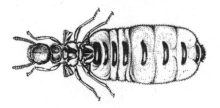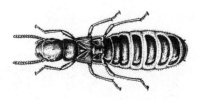

Order ISOPTERA: TERMITE QUEENS and KINGS    258
Not as above.    187

187. (186) Body soft, waist not constricted; 2 short caudal cerci on tip of abdomen; color pale to brown.
Order ISOPTERA: TERMITE WORKERS and SOLDIERS    258

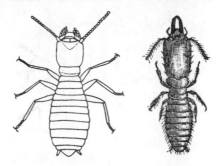

Not as above.    188

188. (187) Large, except very young stages; antennae threadlike, many segmented; nearly as long as to longer than body; face directed downward.
Order ORTHOPTERA: CRICKETS and ROACHES    209

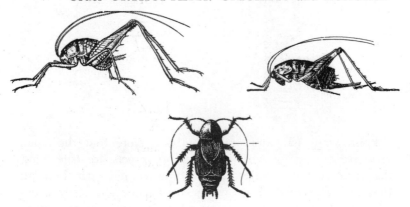

Small, less than 3 mm. long.    189

189. (188) Antennae many segmented, long, 2 basal segments thickened.
Order CORRODENTIA: PSOCIDS or BOOK LICE    264

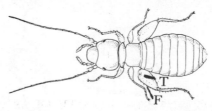

Not as above.    190

190. (189) Antennae short, 2-5 segmented. Attack birds, fowls, and few mammals.

Order MALLOPHAGA: CHEWING LICE    280

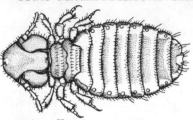

Not as above. Miscellaneous insects attracted to lights, or enter structures by chance.

Not STRUCTURAL PESTS

191. (177) Two wings (1 pair); halteres (balancers) present; sucking, lapping, or piercing mouthparts; lacking filaments at end of body.

Order DIPTERA: TRUE FLIES    685

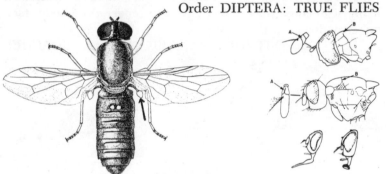

Four wings (2 pairs) (illust. 193). Note that the thickened front wings of various groups of insects are true wings that protect the delicate, more typical hind pair beneath; thus the thickened front wings of Orthoptera, as roaches, crickets, etc. are called tegmina; of Hemiptera, the true bugs, hemelytra; of Coleoptera, the beetles, elytra or wing covers.    192

192. (191) Abdomen ending in a pair of movable pincers or forceps.

Order DERMAPTERA: EARWIGS    256

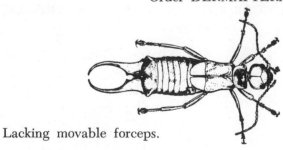

Lacking movable forceps.    193

193. (192) Body delicate; body and wings covered with down and scales that readily rub off; mouthparts a coiled tube for sucking.

Order LEPIDOPTERA: MOTHS    557

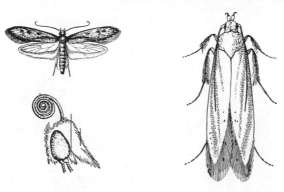

Lacking conspicuous scales or down.    194

194. (193) Body usually hard; wing covers (elytra) meeting in a straight line down the middle of the back, usually covering the abdomen, but may be much shorter; membranous wings beneath elytra.

Order COLEOPTERA: BEETLES, WEEVILS    379

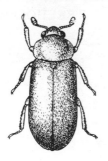

Not as above.    195

195. (194) Front wings (hemelytra) thickened or leathery on basal portion, abruptly thin (membranous), usually overlapping on outer portion; mouthparts a segmented, sucking beak arising at front of head and extending between legs, except when feeding; tarsi of legs with 2 claws.

Order HEMIPTERA: TRUE BUGS    342

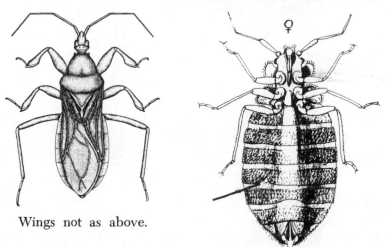

Wings not as above.    196

196. (195) Front wings of uniform texture throughout, the tips not, or but slightly overlapping when at rest; segmented sucking beak arising from hind part of head, often appearing to arise at base of front legs.

Order HOMOPTERA: LEAFHOPPERS,
TREEHOPPERS, etc.    342

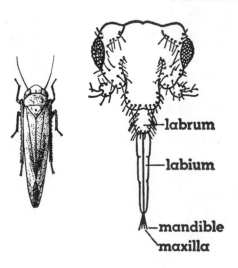

Not as above.    197

197. (196) Large, except very young stages; front wings of adults long and narrow, leathery; hind wings folded fanlike beneath forewings; antennae threadlike, many segmented, at least as long as body; chewing mouthparts.

Order ORTHOPTERA: CRICKETS and ROACHES    209

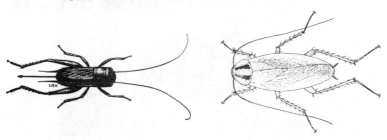

Not as above.    198

198. (197) Wings long and narrow, all similar in form and size, white and translucent, when at rest extending well beyond tip of body; wings deciduous, breaking from body to form short stubs; body yellowish brown to black; chewing mouthparts.

Order ISOPTERA: TERMITE QUEENS and KINGS    258

Wings not as above; front wings larger and longer than hind wings, fore and hind wings often hooked together and may appear as one; wings of female ants deciduous, leaving short stubs; mouthparts for chewing or both chewing and sucking.

Order HYMENOPTERA: ANTS, BEES and WASPS    587

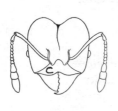

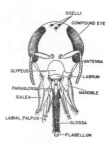

# COLLEMBOLA (Springtails)

199. (180) Body globular to oval; abdomen with 4 basal segments fused, segments V and VI forming a small apical papilla; usually yellowish with black eyes; length 0.25-2.7 mm.

Family SMINTHURIDAE

Body elongate; abdomen with 6 distinct segments. 200

200. (199) Antennae short, 4 segmented; prothorax well developed and visible from above; scales lacking; furculum (spring), when present arising from fourth abdominal segment; length 0.8-3 mm.

Family PODURIDAE: SNOW FLEAS et al.

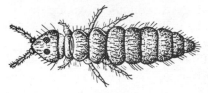

Antennae longer, 4-6 segmented; prothorax reduced, not readily visible from above; covered with hairs or scales; furcula (s), when present, appears to arise from fifth abdominal segment; length about 0.7-6 mm.

Family ENTOMOBRYIDAE

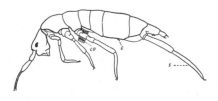

# THYSANURA (Silverfish)

206. (178, 1064) Abdominal sternites (underside) with medial setal combs (tufts of hairs); tergites (upper side) lacking outer dorsal setal combs, leaving 2 rows of setal combs on each side, *or* setae not in combs. 207

Abdominal sternites lacking medial setal combs; tergites
with outer dorsal setal combs, thus having 3 rows of combs
on each side.                                                          208

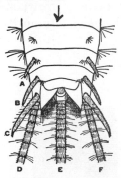
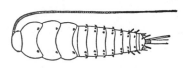

207. (206) Color pattern above mottled gray, pale to tan or brown,
cuticle beneath scales light yellow; maxillary palpus 6 segmented; thoracic and abdominal setae in tufts or combs,
not single; last tergite wider than long; ovipositor visible from
above; 3 pairs of styli (illust. 206, A, B, C) on female, 2 on
male; length of body up to 13 mm. Cosmopolitan, confined
to structures with hot areas.

Firebrat, *Thermobia domestica*

Silver to steel gray to almost black, with metallic sheen,
uniform, cuticle beneath pale; maxillary palpus 5 segmented;
setae above in small groups or single, never in tufts or combs;
last tergite longer than wide; ovipositor not readily visible
from above; 2 pairs of styli (illust. 206 B, C) on both sexes;
length of body up to 13 mm. Cosmopolitan, confined to structures.

Silverfish, *Lepisma saccharina*

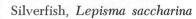

208. (206) Scales uniform gray, cuticle pale beneath; 2 pairs of styli; outer dorsal setal combs on abdominal tergites II-VI (C); last tergite as shown; length of body up to 19 mm. Widespread, more common in South, largely confined to structures.

Gray silverfish, *Ctenolepisma longicaudata* (*urbana*)

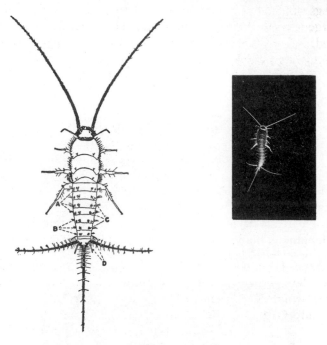

Scales dark gray, with light and dark lengthwise stripes, cuticle beneath pale; 3 pairs of styli (illust. 206 A, B, C); outer dorsal setal combs on tergites II-VII; last tergite as shown; length of body up to 16 mm. Widespread, more common in North.

Four-lined silverfish,
*Ctenolepisma lineata* (*quadriseriata*)

## ORTHOPTERA (Crickets and Roaches)

209. (188, 197) Hind legs fitted for leaping, the femur appreciably enlarged (illust. 210); tarsi 3 or 4 segmented; antennae thread-like, many segmented, as long as or longer than body.     210

All legs similar in form, femur of hind legs not or only slightly enlarged for walking and running; tarsi 5 segmented; body flattened and oval, much longer than wide; antennae thread-like, many segmented, as long as or longer than body.
Family BLATTIDAE: ROACHES     211

210. (209) Tarsi 4 segmented; general body color uniform, light gray to dark brown, light ventrally; back arched (humpbacked); wingless. Basements and damp situations.
Family GRYLLACRIDIDAE: (Tettigoniidae) CAVE or
CAMEL CRICKETS, genus *Ceuthophilus*

Tarsi 3 segmented.

Family GRYLLIDAE:
true CRICKETS     241

## BLATTIDAE (Roaches)

211. (209) Wings fully developed, shorter or longer than abdomen, veins readily visible.

ADULTS    212

Wings immature, wing pads present or lacking, much shorter than abdomen, veins not readily visible.

NYMPHS    231

212. (211) Smaller species; adults less than 18 mm. long (head, thorax and abdomen, or to tips of wings with long-winged forms). 213

Larger species; adults usually more than 22 mm. long, including wings if longer than abdomen. 217

213. (212, 1060) Length of body to tips of wings less than 12 mm.; wings longer than body; wings and thorax with numerous fine black dots. Massachusetts, Rhode Island.

Spotted Mediterranean roach, *Ectobius pallidus*

Length of body, or to tips of wings if longer than body, 12 mm. or more.                                                                    214

214. (213) Wings covering about half of abdomen; pronotum about 3-5 mm. wide; body length usually 17 mm. or more.

Female wood roaches, *Parcoblatta* spp.

Wings covering somewhat more than half of abdomen or longer than abdomen; pronotum less than 4 mm. wide (illust. 215).                                                                                    215

215. (214, 1069) Tan to dark brown, lacking 2 distinct dark stripes on pronotum; wings with pale transverse band at base of wings bordering pronotum, frequently a pale transverse band about 1/3 the length of wing; male long and narrow, the wings covering the abdomen, female broad and short winged; length about 16 mm. (illust. 211 upper also). Widespread, more common in South.

Brown-banded roach, *Supella supellectilium*

Light medium brown to dark brown, wings uniformly brown color, pronotum with 2 distinct dark longitudinal stripes; wings about as long as or longer than abdomen; length 15 mm.         216

216. (215, 1070) Blackish brown line between eyes on front of head. Largely outdoors, enters structures seeking moisture. Southwestern United States.

Field roach, *Blattella vaga*

Lacking blackish line of front of face. Widespread.

German roach, *Blattella germanica*

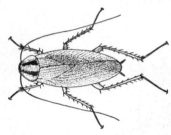

217. (212, 1060, 1062) Color pale green, few black dots near tip of wing; length about 22-24 mm. Tropical, southern tip of Texas. Usually introduced with bananas.

Cuban roach, *Panchlora nivea* (*cubensis*)

Color brown to black.                                                                218

218. (217) Wings shorter than abdomen.                                               219
      Wings longer than abdomen.                        223

219. (218) Large roaches, more than 28 mm. to tip of abdomen.       220
      Usually less than 28 mm. long.                    221

220. (219) Wings very short, mere stubs; dark brown to almost black; very fetid odor; very broad, up to about 24 mm. wide, 38-46 mm. long. An outdoor roach, rarely enters structures. Tropical, Florida.

*Eurycotis floridana*

Wings covering most of abdomen except tip, lobster-like design on thorax; length up to 30-35 mm.; females with shorter wings. Tropical, Florida, Tampa area. Structural pest.

Lobster roach, *Nauphoeta cinerea*

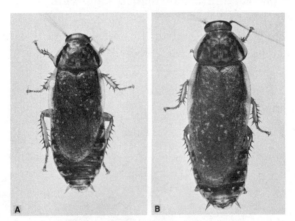

221. (219) Wings shorter than abdomen, covering only 2-3 segments, barely or not reaching abdomen of females, and covering about ¾ of abdomen of males; dark, almost black in color; length 22-30 mm.

Oriental roach, *Blatta orientalis*

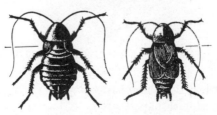

Wings usually covering abdomen, if shorter than abdomen, color brown to dark brown, never black.                    222

222. (221) Pronotum of adults about 3-5 mm. wide, often with paler border; females about 18-20 mm. long, short winged, males about 25 mm. long, long winged. Incidental structural pests.

Wood roaches, *Parcoblatta* spp.

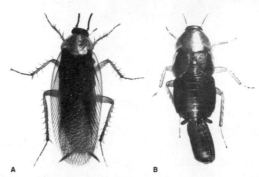

A        B

Pronotum of adults more than 6 mm. wide; wings long.     223

223. (218, 222) Very large, up to 45 mm. or more in length.    224
Smaller, less than 42 mm., brown to black; shiny.    225

224. (223) Dark brown; length 50 mm. or more. Tropical southern Florida.

*Blaberus craniifer*

General color dull grayish brown, wings speckled with black dots, a shield-shaped area on base of wings delimited by a black line and slightly larger than pronotum; very large, nearly 50 mm. New York City area.

Madeira roach, *Leucophaea maderae*

225. (223) Lobster-like design on prothorax; length up to 30-35 mm.; males with wings covering or nearly covering abdomen, females shorter winged. Tropical, Florida, Tampa region. Structural pest.

Lobster roach, *Nauphoeta cinerea*

Lacking lobster-like design.                                        226

226. (225) Front wing with pale yellow streak along outer margin at base; pronotum with dark central area surrounded by pale yellow band; length 25-29 mm.

Australian roach, *Periplaneta australasiae*

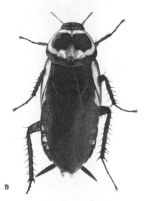

Lacking pale yellow streak on front wings.                    227

227. (226) Pronotum uniform brown to black in color.                228
   Pronotum with a fairly well defined paler area near posterior and lateral margins surrounding a dark central area; general color brown to reddish brown.                                      230


228. (227) Large dark brown roach, 30-35 mm. long; body broad; usually in bananas. Tropical, not established in United States.
                                                *Nyctibora noctivaga*
   Smaller and much narrower.                                        229

229. (228) General color very dark brown to black; pronotum more than 5 mm. wide; length 25-32 mm.
                              Smoky brown roach, *Periplaneta fuliginosa*

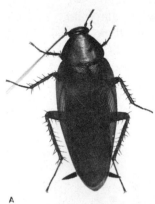

A

   General color light brown; pronotum 3-5 mm. wide; length to tips of wings less than 25 mm.
                              Wood roaches, *Parcoblatta* spp.

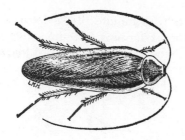

230. (227) Cercus slender and distinctly tapered toward tip, last segment twice as long as wide; antennae about 1½ times the length of body and extending well beyond tips of wings (when not broken); length 32-38 mm.

American roach, *Periplaneta americana*

Cerci broader and rounded laterally toward tip. Last segment not twice as long as wide; antennae extending to or slightly beyond tip of wings; length 32-38 mm.

Brown roach, *Periplaneta brunnea*

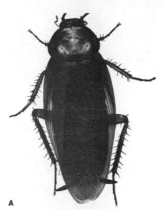

A

231. (211) Early instars with minute black dots at least on thorax; later instars with similar dots, or spines resembling dots, on thorax and abdomen (illust. 232).     232

Lacking dots as above.     233

232. (231) Early instars with minute black dots on head and thorax, the dots on thorax forming lengthwise rows; later instars with dots forming lengthwise rows the full length of the body; general body color shiny light brown; length 9 mm. or less.

Spotted Mediterranean roach, *Ectobius pallidus*

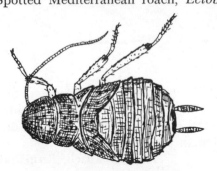

Early and late instars with minute black dots, or minute spines resembling dots, on thorax and abdomen, some of the dots in crosswise rows; general body color dull grayish brown with a light yellow spot near lateral margin of each abdominal segment; length usually 8 mm. or more.

Maderia roach, *Leucophaea maderae*

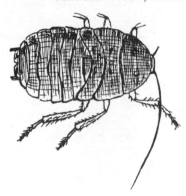

233. (231) First and second instars with thorax dark brown to black, lateral margins pale, meso- and metathorax pale or white, at least in central portion with narrow dark areas near lateral margins, at least on mesothorax; abdomen brown to dark brown; about 2-4 mm. long (illust. 234).                    234

Not as above or larger.                    235

234. (233) Meso- and metathorax with a definite and continuous dark stripe near each margin, margin pale; thorax and abdomen light brown ventrally; length 2-4 mm.

German roach, *Blattella germanica*

Metathorax pale or white for its entire width, at least on posterior half of segment; mesothorax and abdomen with white central area; thorax and abdomen pale or white ventrally; length 2-3 mm.

Brown-banded roach, *Supella supellectilium*

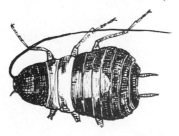

235. (233) Small to late instars with 2 dark longitudinal stripes on pronotum continuous with dark abdomen; abdominal segments usually with pale areas in central portion on dorsal side; length 5-15 mm.

German roach, *Blattella germanica*

Not as above. 236

236. (235) Small to late instars with meso- and metathorax mostly white, the white area usually divided by a dark margin on posterior and lateral margin of mesothorax; dorsally, abdomen with first segment dark brown or black, following 4 segments black laterally; thorax and abdomen pale ventrally; 4-15 mm. in length.

Brown-banded roach, *Supella supellectilium*

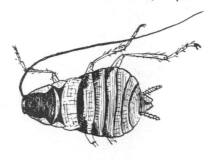

Not as above.                                                                237

237. (236) Early instars shiny reddish brown; cercus rounded laterally and broadly tapering to tip, widest near center; antennae as long as or slightly longer than body; later instars dark reddish brown to black; cercus rounded laterally and broadly tapering to tip, widest near center, about 3 times as long as wide, middle segments about 3 times as wide as long; antennae as long as or slightly longer than body.

Oriental roach, *Blatta orientalis*

Not as above                                                                 238

238.  (237) Early instars uniformly grayish brown dorsally, paler ventrally, shiny; cerci (illust. 230, cerci) slender and distinctly tapered, length about 5 times the width; later instars reddish brown with lateral margins and posterior margins of thorax and lateral (side) abdominal segments somewhat darker (compare with couplet 240); cerci slender, distinctly tapered from near base, length about 5 times the greatest width, widest segments 2½ times as wide as long; antennae uniform brown color throughout.

American roach, *Periplaneta americana*

Early instars dark brown to black, shiny, with pale areas dorsally and on antennae (late instars of brown and smoky brown roaches can be easily confused with the American roach by color alone); cerci broadly rounded laterally, length about 4 times the width, widest segments about 3 times as wide as long. Australian, brown· and smoky brown roaches (illust. 239, 240).                                                                     239

239.  (238) First instar shiny black, second instar very dark brown. Later instarts reddish brown; early instars with mesothorax white or very pale yellow for most of width across body, second abdominal segment with pale or white lateral areas; antennae generally dark, few distal segments of early instars white or pale, basal segments (instars II-VII) pale with few darker segments near center of pale basal third; later instars uniform reddish brown with increasingly noticeable pale or yellow lateral areas on thorax (instar IV+) and lateral margins of abdominal segments (instars VI+).

Australia roach, *Periplaneta australiasiae*

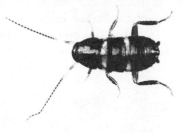

Not as above.                                                                     240

240.  (239) First instar black, second instar dark brown, mesothorax of early instars (I-III) pale or white with dark anterior and posterior margins; lateral areas of second abdominal segment pale or white in early instars (I-III); antennae with 4-5 distal segments white (I-III); later instars reddish brown with

lateral margins and tip of abdomen and posterior margins of thoracic segments noticeably darker; antennae with tips pale (IV-VI), about 10-15 segments pale near the basal fourth of antennae (II-VI) and uniform in color in late instars.

Smoky-brown roach, *Periplaneta fuliginosa*

Early instars brown to dark brown; first instar with lateral margins of abdomen much darker; mesothorax pale or white with dark anterior and posterior margins in instars I-IV; second abdominal segment with pale lateral areas in instars I-V; antennae with 4-5 distal segments white in instars I-II, tips pale in instars III-IV, basal fourth pale in instars I-IV; later instars reddish brown with lateral and posterior margins of segments noticeably darker, paleness on mesothorax, second abdominal segment and antennae fading out.

Brown roach, *Periplaneta brunnea*

241. (210, 1068) General body color straw brown to yellowish brown, head and pronotum darker brown, mottled with paler areas, 3, sometimes 4, dark transverse bands on head between and above and below eyes; nymphs a more mottled grayish brown; adults about 18-20 mm. long. Common in buildings and dumps.

House cricket, *Acheta domestica*

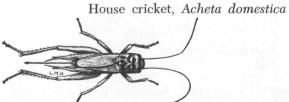

Color dark brown to black, tending toward reddish in paler specimens rather than toward straw color; head without transverse bands.

242

242. (241, 1067, 1068) Adults 14-29 mm. long; wings somewhat shorter than or covering abdomen; nymphs resembling adults, without wings, or with wing pads only; robust. Common in grass, low vegetation and leaf litter. Occasionally invade structures. Much taxonomic confusion regarding species exists.

Large field crickets, *Gryllus* spp.    243

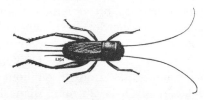

Adults 5-12 mm. long; wings usually shorter than abdomen, mottled brown, reddish brown to black; nymphs resembling adults in form, without wings, or with wing pads only; brownish in color with light and dark longitudinal stripes. Common in grass. Occasionally invade structures. May damage fabrics spread on grass.

Small field crickets, *Nemobius* spp.    248

243. (242) East of 95th meridian.    244
West of 95th meridian.

*Gryllus* spp.: *G. personatus* et al.

244. (243) Pronotum of male widest near hind margin; head of male definitely narrower than pronotum, presenting a retracted appearance, not exceeding 4.7 mm. wide; body length 12.8-19 mm.; ovipositor 9.5-15.5 mm.; both sexes short winged (micropterus).    245

Pronotum of male usually widest near or in front of middle; head of male as often wider than pronotum as not, presenting a swollen rounded (globose) appearance, almost always more than 4.7 mm. wide; body length 15-29 mm. or more; both sexes short winged and long winged.    246

245. (244) Solid black, rarely a dash of reddish on inside or outside of base of hind femora; in leaf litter of deciduous woods. Northern Midwest.

Northern wood cricket, *Gryllus vernalis*

Upper wings always brown; hind femora usually reddish or pale, at least on basal third; tibiae pale; in leaf litter of deciduous woods and pine-deciduous forests, and along forest borders. Eastern United States from Ohio south.

Southern wood cricket, *Gryllus fultoni*

246. (244) Habitat along Atlantic and Gulf Coasts and sandy areas in Southwest; body length usually over 18 mm.; ovipositor 19-23 mm. or more and as often longer than body as not; inhabits flat sandy areas bordering beaches, bare to grassy or shrubbery. East Coast, Maryland to South Carolina.

Beach cricket, *Gryllus firma*

Habitat in fields and grassy areas throughout eastern United States; body length rarely over 23 mm.; ovipositor rarely over 18 mm., and always shorter than body.      247

247. (246) Pronotum usually with reddish or light spots on sides. Southern, occurring northward only in Appalachians and to southern Illinois and Missouri

Triller field cricket, *Gryllus rubens*

Pronotum almost always lacking light spots on sides, except in northern sandy areas such as along Great Lakes. Northern, extending south to just below Appalachians.

Northern field cricket, *Gryllus pennsylvanica*

248. (242) East of 95th meridian.      249
West of 95th meridian.

*Nemobius* spp.

249. (248) Head and pronotal coloration usually strong patterning of dark brown to black with light yellowish; dorsal head striping usually intense and obvious; with short or long wings; inhabit grassy and weedy areas, generally near streams or ponds in moist areas, almost never on high slopes or dry woods; song of males a steady short buzzy, non-musical chirp repeated at about 4-9 per second at 80° F. Eastern North America, Canada to Florida, western extension uncertain.

Striped ground cricket, *Nemobius fasciatus*

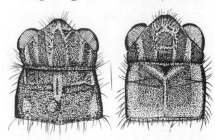

Head and pronotum either sandy reddish or dark reddish brown to black; dorsal head striping faint or lacking; short or long wings; song of males a clear, musical tinkling or trilling; or otherwise different from above.     250

250. (249) General color pale and reddish, especially top of head; short wings only; generally in leaf litter or pine needles; song a slow uninterrupted tinkle, 2-3 per second at 50°, 9-10 per second at 90° F. Eastern United States, Midwest, and Appalachian region to Mississippi and Alabama.

Tinkling ground cricket, *Nemobius tinnulus*

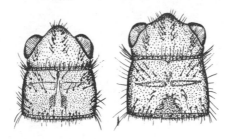

General coloration reddish brown to black; dorsal head striping usually faintly visible; head sandy reddish only in specimens from sandy areas; short and long winged; in lawns, pastures, grassy and weedy areas, well drained; rarely along woodland borders; song a clear musical trill, rapid 6-8 per second at 50°, 16-18 per second at 90° F., and with light breaks at irregular intervals of 2-30 seconds. Eastern North America, Canada to Tennessee, western extension uncertain.

Allard's ground cricket, *Nemobius allardi*

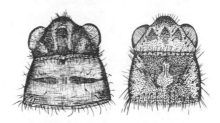

## DERMAPTERA (Earwigs)

256. (184, 192) Front wings short, meeting in a line down the middle of back; larger hind wings folded beneath front wings; body dark reddish brown, head reddish, legs yellowish brown; length 18-20 mm. Readily invade structures. Common in New England, New York, California and Northwest.

European earwig, *Forficula auricularia*

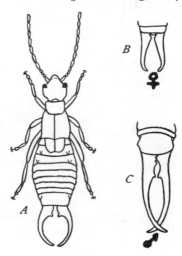

Not as above.                                                                257

257. (256) Dark brown to black, yellowish brown beneath, legs yellowish and ringed with brown stripes, antennae black except third and fourth segments from end, usually white; wingless; length 12-13 mm. Widespread.

Ring-legged earwig, *Euborella annulipes*

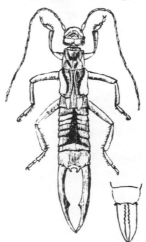

Not as above.

Miscellaneous earwigs, *Labidura riparia* et al.

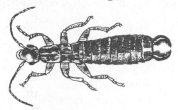

## ISOPTERA (Termites)

258. (186, 187, 198, 1021) Large. *Winged forms* 20-25 mm. or more in length, 4 mm. wide; wings brown and twice as long as body, median vein light, free from fore veins, branches between costa and subcosta, fore wing scale usually not much longer than pronotum; antennae with 24 or more segments, reddish brown to blackish brown; ocelli absent; frontal gland lacking; cerci long. *Soldiers* about 18-20 mm. long, with large reddish brown heads and massive black mandibles, with prominent marginal teeth; head longer than broad, usually not narrowed anteriorly; antennae with at least 23 segments; hind legs with femora swollen (f); cerci very long (compare illust. 261). *Nymphs* yellowish gray brown with mottled gray brown abdomen, which is wider than head. Fecal pellets large and oval, often attached in clumps. Infest damp and rotten wood, which must be damp. Western North America and Southwestern United States.
Family HODOTERMITIDAE: *Zootermopsis* spp.: light Pacific coast rotten-wood termite, *Z. angusticollis*, dark Pacific coast rotten-wood termite, *Z. nevadensis* (a), southwestern rotten-wood termite, *Z. laticeps* (b).

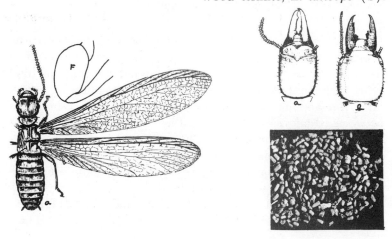

Smaller: *Winged forms* 20 mm. or less, *Soldiers* 15 mm. or less. 259

259. (258) Frontal gland lacking in all castes; empodia (pads) between claws; pronotum flattened, usually broader than head in all castes; no worker caste. *Winged forms* with forewing stub much larger and overlapping posterior stub, not much longer than pronotum, branches between costa and subcostal veins (illust. 261). *Soldiers* with head longer than broad, usually not narrowed anteriorly, *or* short with front concave, with or without prominent marginal teeth. Wood-dwelling; do not build tubes; fecal pellets in galleries. West coast and southern states.

Family KALOTERMITIDAE: DRY, DAMP-WOOD
and POWDER-POST TERMITES    260

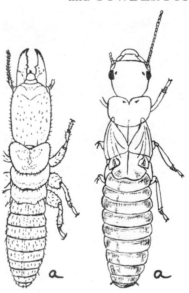

Frontal gland usually present in all castes; worker caste. *Winged forms* (illust. 263) with fore wing stub longer than flat pronotums in Rhinotermitidae, but not overlapping hind scale, and shorter than the saddle-shaped pronotum in Termitidae, fore and hind wing stubs about equal in size; no branches between costal veins. *Soldiers* (illust. 263) with head longer than broad, sometimes markedly narrowed anteriorly; mandibles with or lacking prominent marginal teeth. Subterranean and ground-dwelling termites; tube builders; loose conspicuous fecal pellets absent. Widespread.

Families RHINOTERMITIDAE and TERMITIDAE:
SUBTERRANEAN and DESERT TERMITES    262

260. (259, 1022) All castes small; pellets tiny and scattered about infested wood. *Winged forms* 8.5-10 mm. long, not more than 12 mm. to tips of wings, median vein light, usually united with

subcostal vein near middle of wing. *Soldiers* with short head, front strongly concave (hollowed); usually dark brown to black; mandibles lacking prominent marginal teeth; fore legs lacking spurs on tibiae. Attack woodwork, floors, furniture, common in structures. Southern United States.

Powder-post or furniture termites: *Cryptotermes* spp.: tropical rough-headed powder-post termite, *C. brevis* (a); smooth-headed powder-post termite, *C. cavifrons* (b).

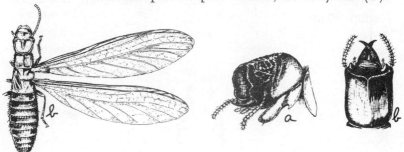

Not as above.                                 261

261. (260, 1022) In sound wood above soil, or in roots in dry situations; fecal pellets well-formed, scattered about and in galleries of infested wood. *Winged forms* about 7.5-20 mm. long, 12-25 mm. to tips of wings; median vein light, free from front veins; ocelli present; antennae with less than 24 segments; abdominal cerci short. *Soldiers* 6-15 mm long; head longer than broad, usually not narrowed anteriorly, reddish or brown, about as wide as body; antennae short, third segment as long as or longer than next two; hind femora swollen (illust. 258f); mandibles black, marginal teeth prominent; cerci short. *Nymphs* pale, whitish gray with mottled abdomen, which is about as wide as head. Western North America and southern United States.

Dry wood termites, *Kalotermes* spp.: western dry wood termite, *K. minor* (illust. 259a) southern dry wood termite, *K. schwartzi* (b), southeastern dry wood termite, *K. snyderi* (c) et al.

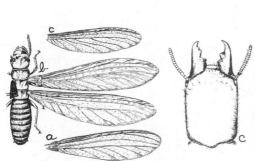
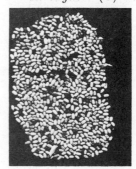

In wood, in or in contact with soil, runways in soil, but do not build tubes from soil to reach wood above soil; lack loose fecal pellets. *Winged forms* dark brown including wings, median vein light, joined with subcosta, membrane clear; length 12 mm. *Soldiers* with low flat heads, longer than broad, not narrowed anteriorly, brown in color; mandibles short and thick, marginal teeth prominent; third antennal segment similar to following segments; femora slightly swollen; length 8-9 mm. Western Plains.

Desert dampwood termite (d),
*Paraneotermes simplicicornis*

262. (259) Small. *Winged forms* 8-10 mm. long, 12-14 mm. to tips of wings, anterior wing stub larger than flat pronotum, wing often reticulate (netted) and with or without hairs; yellowish brown to black. *Soldiers* with head light yellow, elongated, quadrangular, mandibles curved at tip, lacking teeth. *Workers* with thorax narrower than head and abdomen. Soldiers and workers, length 7 mm. or less; pronotum flat and lacking anterior lobes; supplementary reproductives (r) with wing pads (illust. 263 upper also). Build tubes from soil to reach wood. Widespread.

Family RHINOTERMITIDAE: SUBTERRANEAN
TERMITES    263

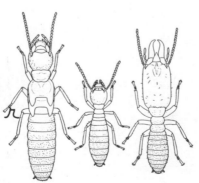

Ground-dwelling termites that live in soil and attack rotten or weathered wood only after covering it with a layer of dark to black fecal material mixed with soil and sand in outer layers and feeding on weathered wood beneath. *Winged forms* with anterior wing stubs shorter than saddle-shaped pronotum; wing only slightly reticulate (netted), if at all, membrane and margin more or less hairy, no branches between costal veins; tibia with 2-3 spines; length up to 13 mm. *Soldiers* with pronotum narrow; head longer than broad, usually narrowed anteriorly; mandible long and straight, tip incurved, marginal tooth small in *Gnathamitermes*, short and curved, tip incurved, marginal tooth large in *Amitermes*. Workers and soldiers with pronotum narrow, with uplifted anterior lobe. Southwestern and western United States.

Desert termites, family TERMITIDAE: *Amitermes* spp.: Snyder desert termite, *A. snyderi*, Wheeler desert termite, *A. wheeleri* (a), *A. minimus* et al; *Gnathamitermes* spp.: tube-building desert termite, *G. tubiformans* (b), *G. perplexus* (c).

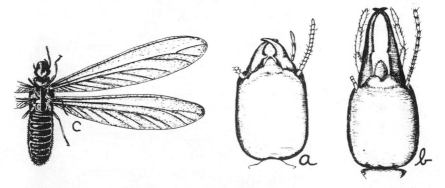

263.  (262, 1020) Ground dwellers, attack wood in or in contact with soil, or can be reached by constructing tubes from soil to wood; must maintain soil connection for water supply, tubes consist of chewed wood, soil, liquid feces and saliva cemented together, liquid fecal specks dot cavities in wood, no fecal

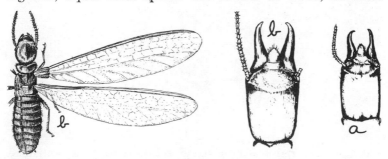

pellets. *Winged forms* brown to black (illust. 186 also); 8-10 mm. long; median vein present, margin more or less ciliate (haired), netted or not. *Soldiers* with head longer than broad, sometimes slightly narrowed anteriorly; frontal gland indistinct, labrum (upper lip) pointed at tip (illust. 262 upper also). Widespread. West and Southwest.

Desert subterranean termite, *Heterotermes aureus;* East to west, subterranean termites, *Reticulotermen* spp.: eastern subterranean termite, *R. flavipes* (illust. 262 upper), western, *R. hesperus* (a), west of Mississippi river to west coastal mountains, *R. tibialis* (b) et al.

Colonies in damp wood, usually rotten and usually on or in soil; galleries in wood contain hardened material composed of chewed wood, excrement, saliva, and some soil particles cemented together. *Winged forms* yellowish brown, median vein absent, margin not ciliate; frontal gland distinct. *Soldiers* with head longer than broad, markedly narrowed anteriorly; mandibles long and slender, lacking prominent teeth; labrum (upper lip) rounded at tip; frontal gland distinct. Southern Florida.

Florida dampwood termite (c), *Prorhinotermes simplex*

## CORRODENTIA (Psocids)

264. (189) Wings (W) lacking or reduced to oval, horny pads, easily confused with nymphal pads (N); legs short, the hind legs less than or scarcely reaching end of abdomen; ocelli lacking.                   265

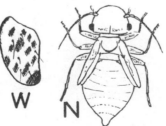

Wings of variable length, never reduced to pads; antennae long; length 0.8-2.4 mm.                   269

265. (264) Completely wingless; eyes minute, far forward and not extending to hind margin of head; femur (F) of hind leg thick and usually with a blunt tooth (T) on front margin; colorless to pale brown. Cosmopolitan, very common.

Book louse, *Liposcelis divinatorius*

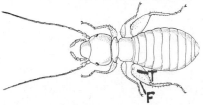

Wings reduced to oval horny pads, often easily broken off (illust. 264W); eyes large and extending to hind margin of head; femur of hind leg not greatly thickened, tooth lacking.    266

266. (265) Brownish to black throughout; wing pads easily lost.

*Lepinotus* spp.    267

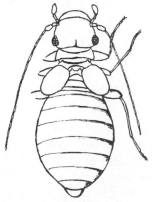

White to pale brown; wings not readily lost.    268

267. (266) Wings horny and scale-like, veins lacking or plainly reticulate (netted); dark, antennae, face and tarsi paler. Widespread, especially in cereals.

Dark booklouse, *Lepinotus inquilinus*

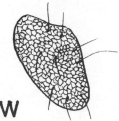

Wings (W) strongly reticulate; dark, abdomen paler; smaller than above.

Reticulate-winged booklouse, *Lepinotus reticulatus*

268. (266) Wings without veins and lacking conspicuous color pattern; reddish brown spots usually evident on abdomen. Produce sound by tapping abdomen, therefore often called death watch. Cosmopolitan.

Larger pale booklouse, *Trogium pulsatorium*

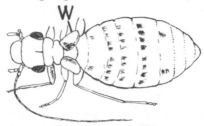

Wings and head with distinctive color pattern; tibiae with 2 transverse bands; body heavily spotted and may appear brown; size and shape as above. Rare.

Spotted-winged booklouse, *Myopsocnema annulata*

269. (264) Fully winged, wings never reduced; antennae more than half the length of body, with 13 segments; eyes dark brown or black, large and extending to back of head; tarsi 2 segmented; ocelli present; light brown to blackish species.          270

Wings variable in length, never reduced to pads; legs long, hind legs extending well beyond end of body; eyes reduced, not extending to back of head, usually pinkish brown; antennae long, with over 20 segments; tarsi 3 segmented; pale to light brown.          272

270. (269) Front wing lacking cubital cell, wing pale brown and iridescent; light brown with black eyes; male with conspicuous, dark, yoke-shaped mating structure above, near tip of abdomen. Not common in structures.

Common shiny-winged psocid, *Ectopsocus pumilis*

Front wing with cubital cell (illust. 271C).          271

271. (270) Pale brown to blackish, abdomen paler, except brown at end and dark intersegmental transverse bands; wings clear with dark veins, usually long, sometimes short; male with book-shaped structures. Cosmopolitan, common in structures.

Cosmopolitan grain psocid, *Lachesilla pedicularia*

Larger than above, ends of veins clouded with brown, giving a somewhat spotted appearance. East of Rockies, not common in structures.

Spotted-winged grain psocid, *Lachesilla nubilis*

272. (269) Ocelli lacking; 4 wings which vary from short to very long; short-winged forms pale with very small eyes; full-winged forms light brown with wings twice as long as abdomen; eyes large, pinkish brown. Moist situations.

Vinegar barrel psocid, *Psyllipsocus ramburii*

Ocelli present; front wings only developed, shorter than abdomen; hind wings mere vestiges; long slender legs; body short, pale brown. 273

273. (272) Front wing broadly rounded, 3 times as long as wide. Southeastern United States.

Small winged southern house psocid,
*Psocathropos lachlani*

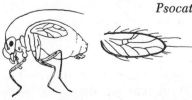

Front wing long and narrow, widest before middle, tapering to tip, 4 times as long as widest portion. Northeastern
United States.

Narrow winged house psocid, *Dorypterex pallida*

## ANOPLURA, MALLOPHAGA (Sucking and Chewing Lice)

The host, and location on host are important aids in identification of lice. The host is usually known or readily ascertained.

280. (183, 190) Sucking mouthparts.

Sucking lice, order ANOPLURA    281

Chewing mouthparts.

Chewing lice, order MALLOPHAGA    302

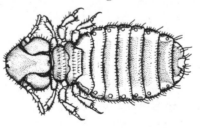

## ANOPLURA (Sucking Lice)

281. (280) Man as host; eyes or eye tubercles present.    282

Land mammals other than man as hosts; eyes lacking. Most
readily identified by host preference.

Family HAEMATOPINIDAE    284

282. (281) Broadly oval, crablike; head small in proportion to
thorax; first pair of legs smallest; first apparent abdominal

segment with 3 pairs of spiracles; abdominal segments with lateral lobes; length 1.5-2 mm.

Family PHTHIRIIDAE: crab louse, *Phthirius pubis*

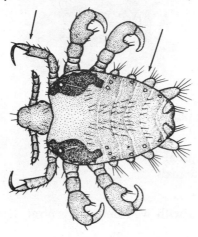

Body elongate, not crablike; head nearly as long as thorax; all legs about same length; first abdominal segment with 1 pair of spiracles; abdominal segments without lateral lobes (illust. 283).

Family PEDICULIDAE    283

283. (282) Under clothing, cling to clothes and lay eggs on clothing; color, grayish brown, but variable; length 2.5-3.5 mm.

Body louse, *Pediculus humanus humanus*

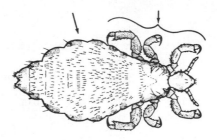

On hair, especially head, but may be on other hairy regions; cling to and lay eggs on hairs; length 2.1-3.2 mm.

Head louse, *Pediculus humanus capitis*

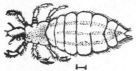

284. (281) Dogs as hosts; length 1.5-2 mm.
Dog sucking louse, *Linognathus setosus*

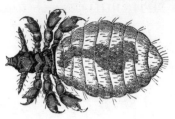

On other mammals. 285

285. (284) Rats as usual hosts. 286
On other mammals. 291

286. (285) Abdomen with well defined ventral, lateral and dorsal plates.

OLDER LICE 287

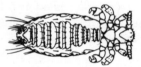

Abdomen with plates absent or poorly defined.

IMMATURE LICE 290

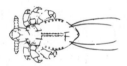

287. (286) Lateral plates small, subtriangular (a); second segment of antennae as long as wide.

Spined rat louse, *Polyplax spinulosa*

Lateral plates large, emarginate posterior (b); second segment of antennae longer than wide.

*Hoplopleura* spp. 288

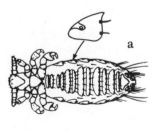
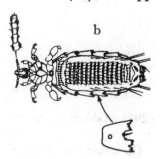

288.  (287) Lateral plates of fourth to sixth segments with 1 large
      and 1 minute hair.

Tropical rat louse, *Hoplopleura oenomydis*

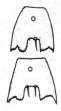

Lateral plates of fourth to sixth segments with 2 similar
large hairs.                                                   289

289.  (288) Lateral plates broadly emarginate, thornlike processes
      at posterior angles.

*Hoplopleura hirsuta*

Lateral plates narrowly emarginate, posterior angles broad
and not thornlike.

*Hoplopleura acanthopus*

290.  (286) Abdomen with spiracles and 2 parallel rows of hairs (a).

Spined rat louse, *Polyplax spinulosa*

Abdomen lacking spiracles and rows of setae (b).

*Hoplopleura* spp.

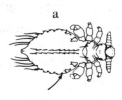
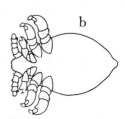

291.  (285) Mice as hosts.

Mouse louse, *Polyplax serrata*

On other mammals.                                              292

292.  (291) Rabbits as hosts.

Rabbit louse, *Haemodipsus ventricosus*

On other mammals.                                              293

293. (292) Horses, mules and asses as hosts; length 2.5-3.5 mm.
      Horse sucking louse, *Haematopinus asini*

On other mammals.                                                                    294

294. (293) Swine as hosts; length 5-6 mm.
      Hog louse, *Haematopinus suis*

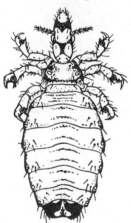

On other mammals.                                                                    295

295. (294) Goats as hosts.                                                           296
      On other mammals.                                                              297

296. (295) Head long and narrow, rounded in front, 2 lateral
      notches, deeply fitted into thorax; length 1.5-2 mm.
            Goat sucking louse, *Linognathus stenopsis*
      Not as above.

African blue louse, *Linognathus africanus*

297. (295) Sheep as hosts.                                        298
      Cattle as hosts.                                            299

298. (297) On body; up to 2.8 mm. long.

Sucking body louse, *Linognathus ovillus*

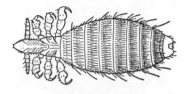

Congregate on legs, especially around dew claws; head short and broad; head and thorax much narrower than abdomen; light in color; length 2 mm.

Sheep foot louse, *Linognathus pedalis*

299. (297) Small; head short and broadly rounded in front; abdomen with prominent tubercles bearing spiracles; length 1.2-1.5 mm. A general resemblance to short-nosed louse.

Small blue louse, *Solenopotes capillatus*

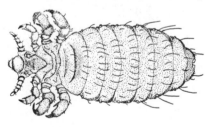

Larger than above when mature.                                    300

300. (299) Head long and slender; body 1/3 as broad as long; thorax as broad as long; length 2-3 mm. Widespread.

Long-nosed cattle louse, *Linognathus vituli*

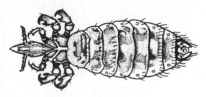

Larger than above when mature.                                    301

301. (300) Head short, nearly as broad as long, bluntly rounded in front; thorax twice as wide as long; head and thorax yellowish brown, abdomen slate blue; length ½ as long as wide, 3.5-4.75 mm. Widespread.

Short-nosed cattle louse, *Haematopinus eurysternus*

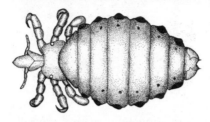

Somewhat larger, usually 5-6 hairs, sometimes 8 or more, at margin of abdominal segments; concentrates on tail. Southern.

Cattle tail louse. *Haematopinus quadripertusus*

## MALLOPHAGA (Chewing Lice)

302. (280) Antennae usually concealed in grooves, more or less clubbed, at least last segment broadly rounded, never pointed; maxillary palpi present.                                       303

Antennae exposed, filiform; maxillary palpus absent.          310

303. (302) Tarsi with 1 claw. On guinea pigs.

Family GYROPIDAE      304

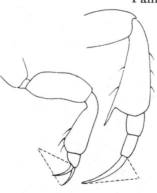

Tarsi with 2 claws. On birds and fowls.                    305

304. (303) Body oval; abdomen broad, little longer than wide, pale yellowish white; head broader than long, bright reddish; length 1 mm.

Oval guinea pig louse, *Gyropus ovalis*

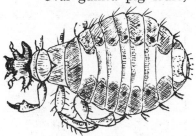

Body long and slender, pale yellow; head and thorax darker; abdomen with darker bands at sutures; length 1.5 mm.

Slender guinea pig louse, *Gliricola porcelli*

305. (303) Antennae lying in cavities which open ventrally (illust. 302); head not broadly triangular or expanded behind eyes.    306
Antennae in grooves on side of head; head broadly triangular, expanded behind eyes. On poultry.

Family MENOPONIDAE    307

306. (305) Sides of head with conspicuous enlargement in front of eye, at base of antennae. On water birds.

Family LAEMOBOTHRIIDAE
Sides of head lacking enlargements. On passerine birds (sparrows).

Family RICINIDAE

307. (305) Adults more than 3 mm. long; color white or dark gray. On ducks and geese.    308
Adults less than 3 mm. long; color yellow. Common on chickens, also on turkeys, peafowls, and ducks.    309

308. (307) Color dark gray; slender; head as broad as long, corners rounded; thorax longer than head; abdomen with dark bands on segments; length 4-5 mm.

Large duck louse. *Trinoton querquedulae*

Color white; broader than above; abdomen bordered with dark spots; length 6 mm.

Goose body louse, *Trinoton anserinum*

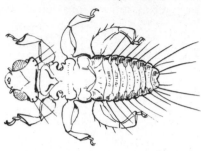

309. (307) At base of feathers on skin, especially below vent and less feathered places; abdomen elongate-oval, males more slender, 2 transverse rows of hairs dorsally per segment; stout and robust; length 2-2.5 mm. Eggs in clusters at base of feathers, especially below vent.

Common chicken body louse, *Menacanthus stramineus*

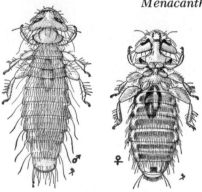

On shafts of feathers; abdomen elongate-oval with a single transverse row of hairs dorsally per segment; legs stout and hairy; length 1.2-1.5 mm. Eggs placed singly at base of feathers between main and after shaft. Common on chickens, occasionally on other fowls.

Shaft louse, *Menopon gallinae*

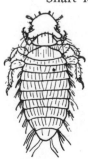

310. (302) Tarsi with 2 claws; antennae 5 segmented. On birds.
Family PHILOPTERIDAE    311

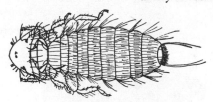

Tarsi with 1 claw; antennae 3 segmented. On mammals.
Family TRICHODECTIDAE    324

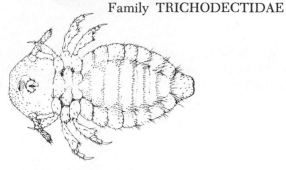

311. (310) Pigeons and turkeys as hosts.                    312
Chickens, ducks and geese as hosts.                          316

312. (311) Pigeons as hosts.                                 313
Turkeys and related fowls as hosts.                          315

313. (312) Very long and slender; head and thorax brownish red,
abdomen dusky; head long and narrow; length 2 mm. Very
common.
Slender pigeon louse, *Columbicola columbae*

Broader, whitish to brown; head broad as or nearly as
broad as long; length 1-2 mm.                                314

314. (313) Broad and brown; head as broad as long, rounded in
front, angular behind; abdomen broad and short; legs stout;
length 2 mm.
*Goniodes damicornis*

Broad oval; whitish to dirty yellow; head nearly as broad as long, rounded in front; thorax narrow; length 1-1.3 mm. Common.

*Goniocotes bidentatus*

315. (312) Head as broad as long, posterior margins extended backward into long projecting stylets; thorax angular and narrowed anteriorly; legs slender and hairy; yellowish white; length 3-3.5 mm. Prominent on neck and breast.

Large turkey louse, *Chelopistes meleagridis*

Head longer than broad, rounded in front, posterior angles rounded; thorax and abdomen narrow and elongate; last abdominal segment of female deeply notched; pale yellow; length 3-3.5 mm.

Slender turkey louse, *Oxylipeurus polytrapezius*

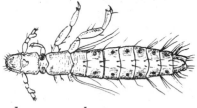

316. (311) Ducks and geese as hosts.    317
     Chickens as common hosts.    320

317. (316) Body short and broad, brownish red; head longer than broad, rounded in front, lower portion expanded and rounded, red; thorax red with darker bands; abdomen oval, whitish in center, dark bands at sides with darker spots at margin; length 1 mm. Common.

*Philopterus icterodes*

     Body slender, elongate.    318

318. (317) Pale yellowish, margin pitchy; abdominal segments with quadrangular bands above; legs dusky above.

Slender goose louse, *Anaticola anseris*

Light yellow with dark border on head, thorax and abdomen; head cone-shaped, rounded in front, longer than broad; abdomen with quadrangular patches on segments; length 4 mm. Common.

Slender duck louse, *Anaticola crassicornis*

320. (316) Smoky gray to dark gray.                                    321
    Pale or reddish brown.                                            323

321. (320) Smoky gray to almost black; head rounded, about as broad as long, circular in front, posterior corners bearing bristles directed outward; thorax narrow; abdomen large, slightly longer than broad, with prominent lateral bands; distributed on feathers over body; length 2.7-3.5 mm. Common.

Large chicken louse, *Goniodes gigas*

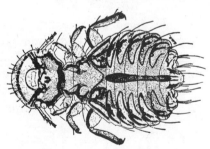

    Much smaller and narrower than above.                             322

322. (321) Slender; head large, rounded in front, longer than broad, margins black, about as wide as abdomen; abdomen long and slender with dark margins, few hairs above; on large wing feathers; length 2 mm.

Wing louse, *Lipeurus caponis*

Broader than above; head longer than broad, rounded in front, broader than eyes; abdomen elongated, oval, median spots on each segment, numerous hairs above; on head and neck, especially young chicks; length 2-2.5 mm. Common.

Chicken head louse, *Cuclotogaster heterographus*

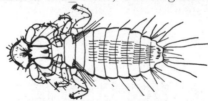

323. (320) Reddish brown, head nearly as long as broad, posterior corners pointed, bearing minute processes; thorax short and much narrower than head and abdomen; abdomen with side markings confluent; on feathers over body, especially under wings and rump area; length 2-3 mm. Rare.

Brown chicken louse, *Goniodes dissimilis*

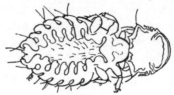

Pale to dirty yellow; head as broad as long, rounded in front, posterior corners bearing 2 long prominent bristles directed backward; abdomen broad and rounded, darker on margins; on fluff and feathers; length 0.8-1.5 mm. Common.

Fluff louse, *Goniocotes gallinae*

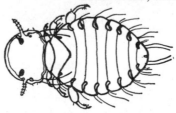

324. (310) Cats as hosts; head pointed, slightly longer than broad; head and thorax bright yellow; abdomen whitish with median bands above; length 1-1.3 mm. Uncommon.

Cat louse, *Felicola subrostrata*

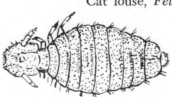

Other mammals as hosts.                                      325

325. (324) Dogs as hosts.                                                    326
     Other mammals as hosts.                                                 327

326. (325) Short and broad, ½ as long as broad; head large, broader
     than long, slightly rounded in front; abdomen broad and globu-
     lar, lacking median bands or spots; clear bright yellow; length
     1-1.3 mm.

                          Dog biting louse, *Trichodectes canis*

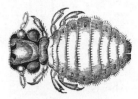

          Larger, 2.3 mm. Common in California.
                                      *Heterodoxus longitarsus*

327. (325) Horses, mules and asses as hosts.                                 328
     Other mammals as hosts.                                                 329

328. (327) Antennae inserted well forward in line with anterior
     margin; head broader than long, rounded in front, wider be-
     hind antennae; abdomen tapers posteriorly, darkened dorsally
     on 7 segments with spots; hairy above and below; yellow in
     color; length about 1.9-2 mm.

                                                *Bovicola pilosus*

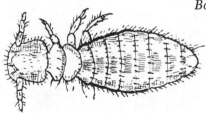

          Antennae inserted well back of front margin of head; head
     slightly longer than broad, front forming a semicircle in front
     of antennae; abdomen oval, 8 dark transverse bands dorsally,
     extending from midline to ½ the distance to lateral margins;
     head, thorax and legs reddish brown, abdomen yellowish;
     length about 2.5 mm.

                          Horse biting louse, *Bovicola equi*

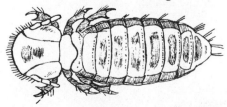

329. (327) Cattle as hosts; broad and flattened; head as broad as long, rounded in front, reddish; abdomen yellowish white, segments marked with median transverse bands; antennae inserted well back and directed backward; length 1-1.5 mm. Common.

Cattle biting louse, *Bovicola bovis*

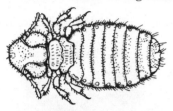

Sheep and goats as hosts. 330

330. (329) Sheep as hosts; head as broad as long, somewhat rounded in front, reddish; abdomen elliptical, whitish, each segment having a median band near the outer border; length 1.5 mm.

Sheep biting louse, *Bovicola ovis*

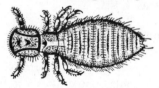

Goats as hosts. 331

331. (330) Common goats as usual hosts; head quadrangular, broader than long; abdomen broad with median dark bands; head and thorax reddish brown, abdomen pale yellow; length 1.5 mm.

Goat biting louse, *Bovicola caprae*

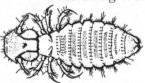

Angora goats as usual host; large, yellow in color; hairy; length 1.5-2 mm. (illust. 310 lower also).

Angora goat biting louse, *Bovicola limbatus*

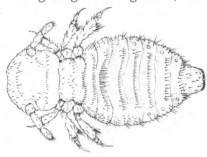

## HEMIPTERA, HOMOPTERA (True Bugs, Leafhoppers)

342. (183, 195, 196) Beak arising from hind part of head, often appearing to arise at base of fore legs; front wings of uniform texture throughout, the tips not or but slightly overlapping when at rest. Primarily plant feeders, attracted to lights. Some leafhoppers and treehoppers. Occasionally bite man.

Order HOMOPTERA: *Erythroneura* spp. *et al.*

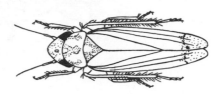

Beak arising from front part of head; tarsi with 2 claws; winged or wingless, the front wings when present leathery at base, membranous at tip. True bugs.

Order HEMIPTERA   343

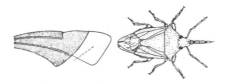

343. (342) Wings lacking or reduced to mere vestiges; body broad and flat, oval in outline; antennae 4 segmented, conspicuous; proboscis 3 segmented, lying in a groove beneath head and thorax (illust. 344 also); ocelli lacking; head broad, short, and broadly attached to thorax; length up to about 5 mm. Attack man, bats and birds.

Family CIMICIDAE: BED BUGS   344

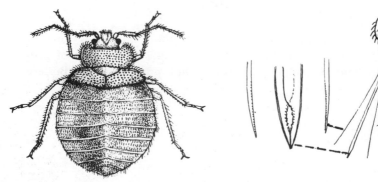

Wings fully developed, occasionally lacking; large elongate bugs; flattened dorsally.    353

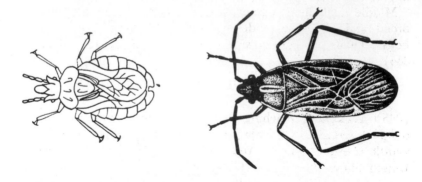

344. (343) Head longer than broad; labrum (upper lip) covering base of beak, much longer than broad; legs very long, femora extending beyond side of body for a distance greater than width of pronotum; organ of Berlese lacking.

*Primicimex cavernis*

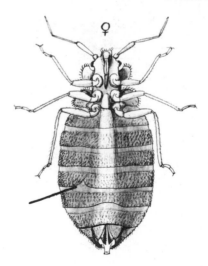

Head longer than broad; labrum short, about as long as broad; legs short, femora not much longer than width of pronotum and projecting slightly beyond sides of body; Berlese organ present.    345

345. (344) Middle and hind coxae close together; metasternum compressed; large bristles of body toothed (dentate) only at tip; Berlese organ dorsal (compare illust. 344).    346

Middle and hind coxae widely separated; metasternum broad and plate-like, widening anteriorly; large bristles of body dentate on convex side; Berlese organ ventral (illust. 344).    349


346. (345) Beak long, reaching to posterior coxae; posterior abdominal tergites in female strongly wavy; Berlese organ at middle of fifth segment. Attacks chickens and man. Southern United States, Mexico.

Poultry bug, *Haematosiphon inodorus*

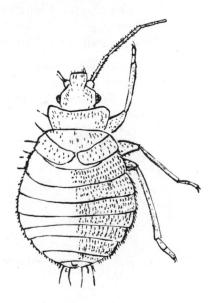

Beak short, reaching to about anterior coxae; posterior abdominal tergites only slightly wavy.    347


347. (346) Pronotum strongly narrowed posteriorly; lower posterior portion of head and adjoining prosternum strongly convex. White-throated swift, western United States.

*Synxenoderus cosmosus*

Not as above.    348

348. (347) Body clothed with long bristles, sides of abdomen with some bristles twice as long as width of eye. Gray-breasted martin and other swallows; western United States. Occasionally attacks man.

*Hesperocimex coloradoensis*

Body clothed with short, inconspicuous bristles, those of sides much shorter than width of eye. Chimney swift. Eastern and central United States.

Chimney swift bug, *Cimexopsis nyctalis*

349. (345) Pubescence (fine hairs) long, fine, and silky; last 2 antennal segments about equal in length.

Swallow bug, *Oeciacus vicarius*

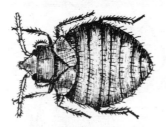

Pubescence short, stiff; third antennal segment longer than fourth.

*Cimex* spp.   350

350. (349) Sides of pronotum not widely dilated or reflexed, fringed with sparse, nearly straight hairs; vestige of front wing distinctly rounded. Man. Tropical.

Tropical bed bug, *Cimex hemipterus*

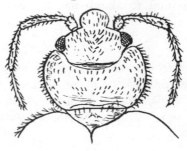

Sides of pronotum widely dilated, broader than width of eye, densely fringed with backward-curved hairs; back margins of fore wing rounded at inner angles only.          351

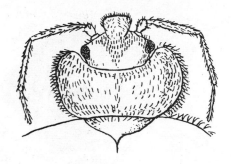

351. (350) Length of contiguous portions of reduced fore wing shorter than scutellum; second antennal segment shorter than third; fringe hairs of pronotum margin shorter than width of eye, length up to 5 mm. Man. Temperate regions.

Bed bug, *Cimex lectularius*

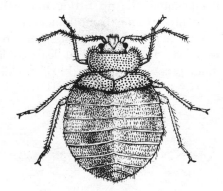

Length of contiguous portions of wing vestiges longer than scutellum; second and third antennal segments equal in length; fringe hairs of pronotum longer than width of eye.          352

352. (351) Marginal hairs relatively long; abdomen with transverse lines dorsally. Bats. Eastern North America.

*Cimex adjunctus*

Marginal hairs relatively short; transverse lines absent. Bats. Western North America.

*Cimex pilosellus*

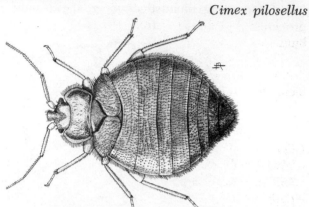

353. (343) Usually winged, attack mammals in structures and elsewhere.                                                                                              354

Winged; do not attack man or pets. Attracted to lights or enter structures for hibernation.                                                                          355

354. (353) Beak 3 segmented, the tip fitting into a median longitudinal groove in prosternum; front femora more or less enlarged for grasping, less than half as long as broad; claws at end of tarsi; antennae 4 segmented, at least as long as head; head shorter than pronotum. Large blood-sucking bugs.

Family REDUVIIDAE: CONENOSES    357

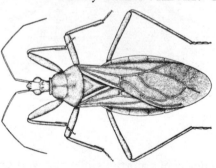

Bugs that bite when caught or harmed, or only incidentally; predatory on insects. Attracted to structures by lights, or incidental.

PREDATORY HEMIPTERA

355. (353) Beak long and slender, 4 segmented, the first segment long; front femora not thickened; claws at end of tarsi; antennae 4 segmented, at least as long as head; head shorter than pronotum; membrane of front wing with many veins; elongate bugs.

Family COREIDAE    356

Not as above. Largely plant feeders, attracted to lights, or incidental in structures.

Miscellaneous HEMIPTERA

356. (355) Flattened bugs, narrowly oval in shape; adults brownish-black with 3 red stripes on thorax and red veins on wings; young nymphs bright red, older nymphs resembling adults; length up to 11-14 mm. Plant feeders on boxelder and other maples, and a few other trees. Seldom attack man. Enter structures for hibernation.

Boxelder bug, *Leptocoris trivittatus*

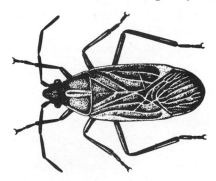

Elongate, flattened bugs; adults grayish black, nymphs ashygray with black appendages; length 22-25 mm. Plant feeders on cucurbits. Enter structures for hibernation.

Squash bug, *Anasa tristis*

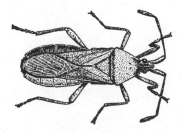

357. (354) Front wing with quadrangular or discoidal cell (illust. 358) at base of membrane.    358

Front wing lacking the quadrangular cell.    363

358.   (357) Ocelli further apart than eyes.  Southwestern United States, Mexico.

Genus *Apiomerus*: *A. spissipes et al.*

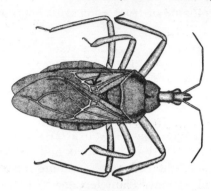

Ocelli closer together than the eyes.                                             359

359.   (358) Sides of mesosternum (carries second pair of legs) without a tubercle or fold in front; first segment of beak about as long as front portion of head; length 13-16 mm.

Genus *Zelus*: *Z. socius, Z. exsanguis et al.*

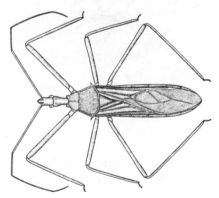

Sides of mesosternum lacking tubercle or fold in front of hind angles of prosternum; first segment of beak longer than front portion of head.                                                          360

360.   (359) Front femur thickened, densely granulate; hind femur unarmed (illust. 361).                                                      361

Front femur unarmed, not at all or only slightly thickened, slightly granulated.                                                            362

361.   (360) Front tibia armed with spines ventrally; wing as figured; length 13-14 mm.

Genus *Sinea*: *S. diadema*

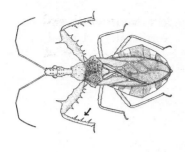 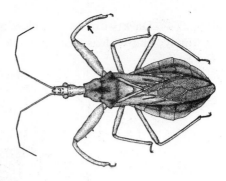

Front tibia unarmed; length 14 mm.

Genus *Acholla*

362. (360) Pronotum extended backward over scutellum with a high median, tuberculate ridge; robust. Widespread.

Wheel bug, *Arilus cristatus*

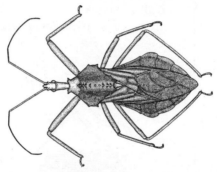

Pronotal lobe six-sided, not elevated or extended backward.

Genus *Rhynocoris*

363. (357) Pronotum usually constricted behind the middle (illust. 365); front coxa flat or concave on outer sides; middle tibia with spongy fossa (grooves).    364

Pronotum constricted on or before the middle (illust. 367); front coxae not flattened, the outer sides convex, first tarsi 3 segmented.    367

364. (363) Apical portion of front tibia angulately dilated beneath; spongy fossa being preceded by a small prominence (illus. 365).

Genus *Melanolestes*   365

Tibia not dilated; spongy fossa elongate; front wing with corium and membrane (illust. 366), each marked with a yellow spot.

Two-spotted corsairs, *Rasahus* spp   366

365. (364) Dark to black in color; often wingless, front wings entirely black; legs and antennae dark. Northeastern United States.

Black corsair, *Melanolestes picipes*

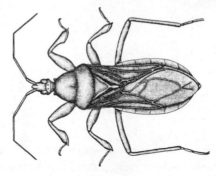

Sides of abdomen red, upper surface more or less red; length 13-14 mm. Southern United States.

*Melanolestes abdominalis*

366. (364) Southern states.

*Rasahus biguttatus*

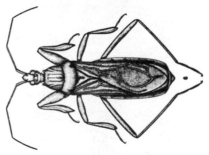

Northwest, California.

*rasahus thoracicus*

367. (363) Antennae inserted on top of head between the margins, close to eyes; lacking antenniferous tubercles projecting from side of head; disk of pronotum unarmed; apex of scutellum produced into a spine; beak stout, distinctly curved; front of head turned downward (illust. 368).

Genus *Reduvius* spp.    368

Antennae inserted on side of head near its margins; antenniferous tubercles projecting slightly from side of head; beak slender and relatively straight; head moderately long with antennae inserted behind the top of head (illust. 369).

Genus *Triatoma* spp.    369

368. (367) Dark in color; covered with fine hairs; nymphs covered with dust and dirt; length 15-20 mm. Widely distributed, especially Midwest and East.

Masked hunter, *Reduvius personatus*

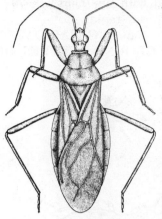

Yellowish brown. Southwest.

*Reduvius senilus*

369. (367) Southern United States; length 25 mm.

Bloodsucking conenose,
*Triatoma sanguisuga* et al.

Western United States.

*Triatoma protracta* et al.

## COLEOPTERA (Beetles, Weevils)

The structural pest families of beetles are given in couplets 379-415, which lead into couplet 416 and later for identification to species by habitat and evident characters as color, length of antennae, etc. Turn directly to couplet 416 if the food habits are known.

379. (194) Elongate terrestrial beetles; usually 6, occasionally 7, ventral abdominal segments, the first completely divided by hind coxae (illust. 382); antennae filiform, 11 segmented with at least the last 6 pubescent (covered with fine hairs); head almost always narrower than thorax; run rapidly.

Family CARABIDAE:
GROUND BEETLES 416, 456

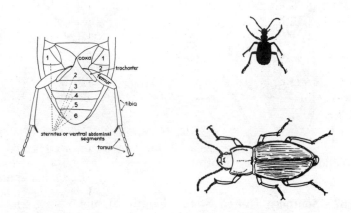

Not as above.                                                                   380

380. (379) Wings, including elytra (wing covers) lacking (illust. 381 upper).                                                             381

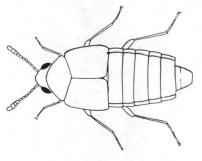

Elytra present, sometimes shorter than abdomen; a line between elytra down the middle of back.                                  382

381. (380, 411, 514) Median ocellus (illust. 392 also) on front of head.

Family DERMESTIDAE:
female odd beetle, *Thylodrias contractus*

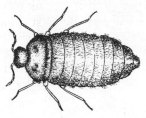

Median ocellus lacking; antennae comblike on both sides; typically without wings. Cockroach egg parasite.

 Family RHIPIPHORIDAE:
*Rhipidius pectinicornis*    411

382. (380) Abdomen with 7 visible segments ventrally, the first completely divided by coxae at the middle; head with median ocellus.

Family DERMESTIDAE:
male odd beetle, *Thylodrias contractus*

Abdomen usually with 7 or less segments ventrally (illust. 385 lower), the first segment never completely divided by coxae.    383

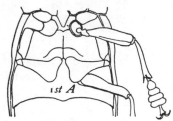

383. (382) Head not prolonged to form a distinct snout (beak); the gular sutures (gs) on under side of head separated and enclosing a gular area (g); prothorax in front of coxae with distinct suture (line) between prosternum (s) and ventral part of pronotum (n).    384

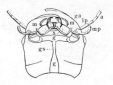 

Head often prolonged into a snout; gular sutures (gs) on under side of head fused into one or lacking; all tarsi 5 segmented, the fourth being minute and more or less concealed by the spreading third segment; prothorax in front coxae lacking suture (line) between posternum (s) and pronotum.

Suborder RHYNCHOPHORA  414

  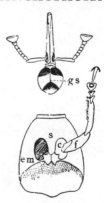

384. (383) Prosternal spine received in a cavity in mesosternum.  385
     Prosternal spine lacking.  386

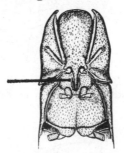

385. (384) First and second abdominal segments firmly fused ventrally; prothorax fitting close to elytra restricting free movement.

Family BUPRESTIDAE:
METALLIC WOOD BORERS  416, 432

Abdominal segments not fused; prothorax loosely joined to mesothorax, permitting free movement; when prosternal spine snaps into mesosternal groove, the body is flipped into the air. Incidental in structures.

Family ELATERIDAE:
CLICK BEETLES 416, 456

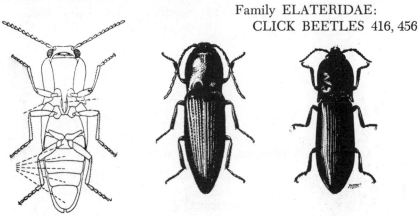

386. (384, 542) Antennae not clubbed, *or* if clubbed the club never round and compact or lamellate (extended and folded on 1 side); elytra (hard wing covers) covering only a portion of the abdomen exposing 2 or more segments, often more than half; abdomen with 6 or 7 segments visible ventrally, flexible and tip often turned upward, segments horny (thickened) above.

Family STAPHYLINIDAE:
ROVE BEETLES 416, 542

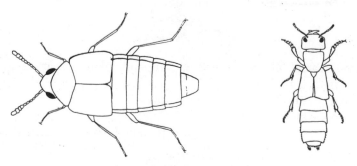

Elytra usually covering abdomen, or rarely leaving more than 2 segments exposed, if more than 1 is exposed the antennal club is compact. 387

387, (386) Antennae elbowed, with long first segment, club compact; elytra truncate (squared) at tips, short, leaving 2 segments exposed; body hard, short and stout, shiny, black or red and black.

Family HISTERIDAE

 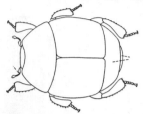

Antennae not elbowed, with or without a club. 388

388. (387) All tarsi with 3 or less segments. 389

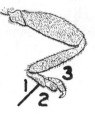

Some tarsi with 4 or more segments. 390

389. (388) Tarsal claws toothed or appendiculate (bearing appendages); first ventral abdominal segment with distinct curved coxal lines. Enter structures for hibernation; often seen on windows.

Family COCCINELLIDAE:
LADY BEETLES 416

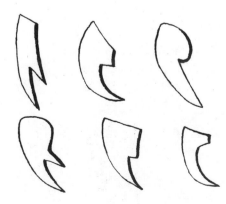  

Tarsal claws simple; ventral segment lacking coxal lines; first and second tarsi sometimes with 2 segments.

Families LATHRIDIIDAE,
few ENDOMYCHIDAE    416

390. (388) First and second tarsi 5 segmented, third tarsi 4 segmented (illust. 391).    409

Tarsal segments practically never as above.    391

391. (390) Tarsi less than 5 segmented, *or,* if 5 segmented, the fourth segment not concealed, *or,* if 5 segmented and the fourth minute or more or less concealed by the third segment the antennae have a distinct club.    392

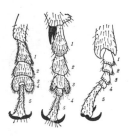

Tarsi apparently 4 segmented, but actually 5 segmented, the fourth being minute and more or less concealed in a dorsal groove or very deep apical emargination of the third segment, third segment strongly dilated and densely pubescent beneath (illust. 388); antennae without a sharply differentiated club, usually filiform, serrate or pectinate.    412

392. (391) Head with a median ocellus.
Family DERMESTIDAE:
CARPET BEETLES 416, 456

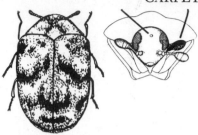

Median ocellus lacking. 393

393. (392) Prothorax with a deep dorso-apical groove for reception of antennae on each side (illust. 392 also); antennae 10 segmented with large 1 segmented club; tarsi 4 segmented; body broadly oval convex, shiny; length less than 1.5 mm.
Family MURMIDIIDAE 456, 512

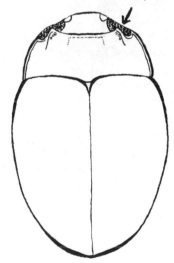

Prothorax lacking dorso-apical groove for antennae. 394

394. (393) Front and middle tarsi 4 segmented, except most males with 3 segmented tarsi (illust. 391 tarsi). 395
Front and middle tarsi 5 segmented, sometimes with fourth segment very minute, or the basal (first) segment very minute. 396

395. (394) Tarsi 4 segmented, the third segment much smaller than second; pronotum with a complete sublateral (near side) carina (ridge) on each side; body clothed with hairs; length 1.5-1.8 mm.
Family MYCETAEIDAE:
hairy cellar beetle, *Mycetaea hirta* 456, 519

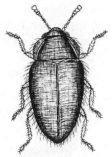

Tarsi 4 segmented, except front tarsi of males 3 segmented; pronotum lacking sublateral carinae; body moderately depressed, densely pubescent.

Family MYCETOPHAGIDAE:
FUNGUS BEEETLES    416

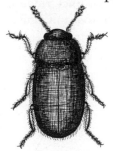

396. (394) Front coxae strongly projecting, elongate or conical but not transverse, usually contiguous (a, c) (close together or touching); pronotum not prolonged over head; trochanters joined to side of femora; elytra usually soft or fairly so, pubescent (finely haired) and with ends rarely truncated (squared).    397

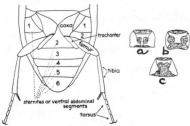

Front coxae not or scarcely projecting, round or transverse, but if strongly projecting and conical the pronotum is prolonged over the head, *or* the trochanters are joined at or near end of femora.    399

397. (396) Hind coxae with a large cavity (illust. 382 lower) for reception of femur; antennae short with large, compact 3 segmented club; body densely pubescent; length 5.5-12.5 mm.

Family DERMESTIDAE:
hide beetles, *Dermestes* spp. 416, 456

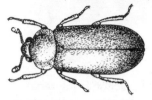

Hind coxae lacking distinct cavity for reception of femur. 398

398. (397) Claws toothed; tarsi with fourth segment very minute; pronotum always with distinct ridge or margin on each side; elytra metallic blue, or red and blue.

Family CORYNETIDAE
(CLERIDAE) 416, 485

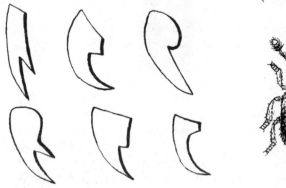

Claws not toothed; pronotum with or without margins; tarsi with basal segment dilated and densely pubescent, or with membranous lobes, except *Thaneroclerus*, which lacks dilated and membranous lobes, but has first segment very much shorter than second.

Family CLERIDAE:
CHECKERED BEETLES 416

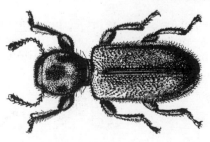

399. (396) Trochanters joined to end of femora, often very long; body strongly convex and nearly always densely pubescent; front coxae conical and often strongly projecting; tarsi with basal segment long, fourth only slightly shorter than third.   400

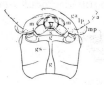 

Trochanters joined to side of femora.                401

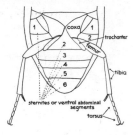

400. (399) Antennae usually with a loose but distinct apical club, or else serrate (saw-like), bases of antennae usually widely separated and nearly in front of eyes; pronotum usually with distinct lateral margins.

Family ANOBIIDAE   416

 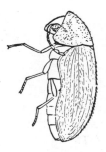 

Antennae filiform, apical segment not thickened, bases of antennae usually very close together and each considerably mesad (toward center) to eye; pronotum not margined.

Family PTINIDAE   416

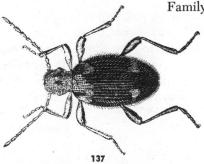

401. (399) Front coxae (illust. 402) strongly projecting, conical and contiguous (touching) or nearly so; pronotum hood-shaped and more or less concealing the head, which is deflexed (turned under); body cylindrical; pronotum often tuberculate (spined); tarsi with basal segment very minute, so that tarsi appear 4 segmented.

Family BOSTRICHIDAE:
FALSE POWDER POST BEETLES    416

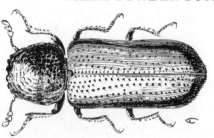

Front coxae not strongly projecting, or if large and slightly projecting, they are transverse and separated, not conical and contiguous; pronotum not hood-shaped or concealing head; head not deflexed.    402

402. (401) Front coxae large and transverse with trochanters partly external.    403

Front coxae small, round and globose, except large and globose in some Lyctidae (powder post beetles); trochanters entirely concealed.    404

403. (402) Hind coxae contiguous (touching) or only very narrowly separated; tarsi with basal segment very minute and fourth but little shorter than third; maxilla with galea (g) and lacinia (f) distinct; antennae usually with loose 3 segmented club, often asymmetrical (one-sided) club; elytra always covering abdomen; body usually somewhat flattened and sometimes strongly flattened.

Family OSTOMATIDAE 416, 456

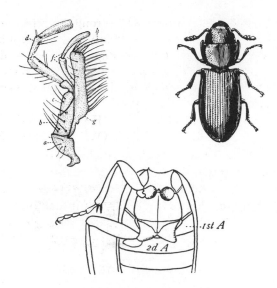

Hind coxae widely separated, usually much more so than middle coxae; tarsi with basal segment about as long as or longer than second, fourth segment distinctly narrower and shorter than third, often minute; maxilla with single lobe (f & g united); antennae with compact 3 segmented club; elytra often truncate and exposing 1 or 2 segments; body usually moderately convex.

Family NITIDULIDAE 416, 456

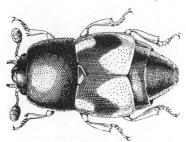

404. (402) Antennae 11 segmented with large, abrupt, fairly compact, 2 segmented club; body elongate, parallel-sided and flattened to moderately convex; first ventral abdominal segment much elongated; dorsal surface nearly smooth or with scalelike hairs; tarsi with basal segment very minute.

Family LYCTIDAE:
POWDER POST BEETLES    416

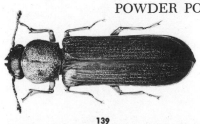

Antennae 11 segmented, either filiform or with a 3 segmented club, occasionally 2 segmented.                    405

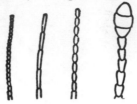

405. (404) Tarsi with basal (first) segment much shorter than second, fourth segment but little smaller than third, male with hind tarsi usually 4 segmented; body very flattened; antennae sometimes filiform; front coxal cavities usually closed, but sometimes open behind; tibiae with well developed spurs; mesosternal epimerons (illust. 406 upper) reaching middle coxal cavities.

Families SILVANIDAE, CUCUJIDAE 416, 456

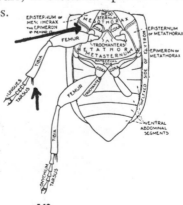

Tarsi with basal segment never minute, usually about as long as or longer than second, fourth segment often minute; antennae always clubbed.                    406

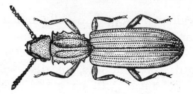

406. (405) Front coxal cavities open behind (b); tibiae with well developed apical spurs; mesosternal epimeron not attaining middle coxal cavities.                    407

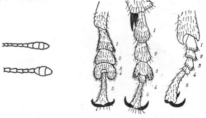

140

Front coxal cavities closed behind (a); tibiae lacking apical spurs; mesosternal epimeron attaining middle coxal cavities.     408

407.  (406, 538) Pronotum with short longitudinal carina (ridge) or sulcus (groove) on each side of middle at base; body elongate, moderately convex, nearly glabrous (smooth), shining; dark brown to rufo-piceus (reddish black); tarsi with fourth segment about half as long as and much narrower than third, first 3 segments of front tarsi feebly dilated and densely pubescent beneath; length 4-4.5 mm.

Family EROTYLIDAE:
Mexican grain beetle, *Pharaxonotha kirschi* 416, 538

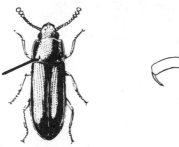

Pronotum lacking basal longitudinal carina (ridge); tarsi lacking hairy ventral pads and ventral membranous projections, 5 segmented except some males with third tarsi 4 segmented; length 2-3 mm.

Family CRYPTOPHAGIDAE     416

408. (406) Lateral margins of pronotum nearly always with at least apical (hind) angle toothed, often with numerous teeth; body often strongly flattened.

Family SILVANIDAE (CUCUJIDAE in part):
FLAT GRAIN BEETLES    416

Lateral margin of pronotum smooth, without teeth; body moderately convex and bearing a close resemblance in shape as well as pubescence to *Cryptophagus* spp.; length 2-2.3 mm.

Family EROTYLIDAE: *Cryptophilus integer*    416

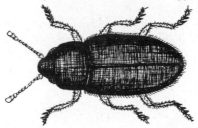

409. (390) Prothorax with a short, narrow apical neck so that head is never even partly received into an anterior cavity in prothorax; brightly colored; length 2-5 mm.

Family ANTHICIDAE 416, 544

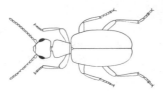

Prothorax lacking apical neck but with an apical cavity into which head is at least partly received.    410

410. (409) Front coxal cavities closed (a) behind (structural pests), with few exceptions (not structural pests); eyes nearly always partly divided by a dilated ridge-like lateral margin of front of head; smooth above.

Family TENEBRIONIDAE 416, 456

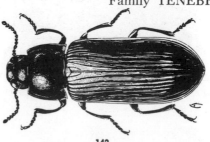

Front coxal cavities open (b) behind. 411

411. (381, 410) Head very strongly constricted at base so that the neck thus formed is 1/3 or less than 1/3 as broad as head; ventral surface strongly convex; tarsi with penultimate (next to last) segment not broadly dilated or densely pubescent beneath.

Family RHIPIPHORIDAE: roach parasites 381

Head not, or scarcely constricted at base; ventral surface feebly convex; tarsi with penultimate segment broadly dilated and pubescent beneath; prothorax lacking distinct lateral margins; middle coxae very prominent.

Family OEDEMERIDAE: WOOD BORERS 416

412. (391) Body narrow and elongate; antennae long, at least reaching to abdomen, often as long as to longer than body; bases of antennae partly surrounded by the eyes; tibiae with apical spurs.

Family CERAMBYCIDAE:
LONG HORNED WOOD BORERS 416

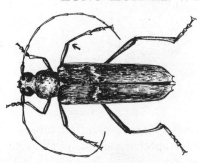

Body usually short, more or less oval, sometimes elongate; antennae short and not surrounded by eyes; tibiae without apical spurs. 413

413. (412) Front of head prolonged slightly into a broad quadrate (4 sided) beak, hardly recognizable as a beak; elytra short and exposing tip of steeply inclined abdomen; hind femora usually greatly thickened, often toothed; body oval to stout.

Family BRUCHIDAE (MYLABRIDAE):
SEED WEEVILS 416, 456

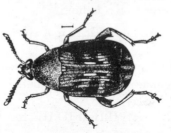

Front not prolonged into a beak; abdomen entirely covered by elytra; tibiae without spurs, *or* if spurred, the antennae are short and more or less clubbed. Accidental in structures, or enter for hibernation only.

Family CHRYSOMELIDAE:
elm leaf beetle, *Galerucella xanthomelaena*

414. (383) Head not prolonged in front of eyes to form a beak; labrum (upper lip) distinct, visible and movable; antennae long, slender, straight and with loose, rarely compact, 3 segmented club; pronotum with lateral margin carinate (ridged), at least at base; abdomen with tip exposed by elytra; tarsi lacking densely pubescent pads on under side of 2 basal segments.

Family PLATYSTOMIDAE (Anthribidae):
FUNGOUS BEETLES 456, 519

Head prolonged or not prolonged into a beak; labrum not externally visible; antennae usually elbowed and with compact club; pronotum usually lacking a distinct margin and margin, if present, rarely carinate (ridged); tip of abdomen exposed or concealed; tarsi usually with densely pubescent pads on under side of 2 basal segments. 415

415. (414) Head prolonged into a downward curved beak, which is usually long and narrow; front tibiae cylindrical near apex (tip) and with dorsal margin not serrate or toothed in species in structures; antennae almost always elbowed.

Family CURCULIONIDAE: SNOUT BEETLES, WEEVILS    416

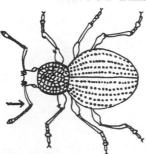

Head not prolonged; front tibiae somewhat antero-posteriorly (front to back) flattened near apex and with dorsal margin always serrate or toothed; antennae always elbowed. Infest wood.

Family SCOLYTIDAE: ENGRAVER BEETLES    445

416. (379, 415) Wood infesting beetles.                              417
     Other than wood infesting.                                     456

417. (416) Elongate, more or less cylindrical; antennae at least 1/3 the body length to longer than body; tarsi apparently 4 segmented, usually with dense cushion-like pubescence beneath on first 3 segments, the third divided, with prongs extending along base of tarsus hiding the minute fourth segment; medium to large beetles (illust. 418 also).

Families OEDEMERIDAE, CERAMBYCIDAE    418

Antennae less than half as long as body; tarsi not as above.    432

418. (417, 1026, 1035) Antennae about half as long as body; body elongated, somewhat flattened; tarsi 4 segmented, but resembling those of Cerambycidae; elytra yellowish brown with dark tips; length about 12 mm.

Family OEDEMERIDAE:
wharf borer, *Nacerda melanura*

Antennae 1/3 body length or more; tarsi 5 segmented (apparently 4), the fourth minute and hidden between prongs of the third segment; medium to large.

Family CERAMBYCIDAE:
LONG-HORNED WOOD BORERS       419
(A number of species of Cerambycidae emerge from firewood in structures, but otherwise are not structural pests and may not be identified below.)

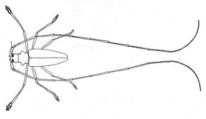

419. (418) Antennae as long as or longer than body (illust. 418 lower).                                                                         420
Antennae less than length of body.                          423

420. (419) Light brown to tan, elongate, cylindrical; each elytra terminating in 2 spines, 2 ivory-colored spots at base and 2 near center; 2 small dark red spots on thorax; antennae as long as to 1/4 longer than body; length 16-22 mm. May emerge from flooring and furniture.

Ivory-spotted borer, *Eburia quadrigeminata*

Lacking ivory spots.                                        421

421. (420) Brown, elongate, cylindrical; yellowish oblique band, at least a light yellow spot, on each elytron, 2 fine teeth at end of each elytron; antennae as long as to 2 times body length; length about 25 mm. Attack fresh cut wood with bark and emerge from firewood.

Banded hickory borer, *Chion cinctus*

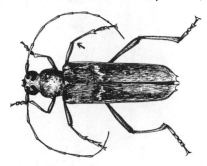

Gray to brown, mottled, with long antennae; length 25-50 mm.

Sawyers, *Monochamus* spp.    422

422. (421) Grayish brown, marbled with white and brown; antennae of female longer than body, of male 2-3 times body length; length 25-30 mm. Emerge from lumber and firewood.
Southern pine sawyer, *Monochamus titillator*
Cloudy gray beetles, mottled and dotted with light to dark brown spots; antennae long; length 37-50 mm. Emerge from lumber and firewood.

Pine sawyer, *Monochamus confusor*

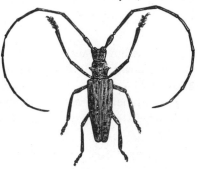

423. (419) Yellow to reddish brown.                                    424
Blue, deep purple, or brownish black to black.            425

424. (423) Flat, amber colored; length about 9.5 mm. Attack oak flooring and woodwork.

Flat oak borer, *Smodicum cucujiforme*

Reddish brown, slender, cylindrical; 4 yellow bands across elytra, the one at base sometimes fading; legs long and reddish; length 6.5-18 mm. Attack fresh lumber with bark and firewood.

Red-headed ash borer, *Neoclytus acuminatus*

425. (423) Deep purple, 3 yellow bands across elytra, 3 narrow yellow lines across prothorax; length 12-15 mm. Attack wood with bark and firewood.

Gray-banded ash borer, *Neoclytus caprea*

Bright blue or black in color. 426

426. (425) Bright metallic blue or bluish black, antennae and legs blackish to black; length 12-14 mm. Attack wood with bark.

Pine borer, *Callidium antennatum*

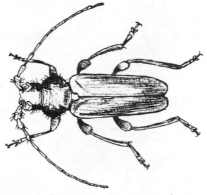

Dark brown to black.                                               427

427. (426) Large, elongate, brownish black with gray pubescence,
forming transverse bands on elytra; length 18-25 mm. Attack
dry, well seasoned wood.

Old house borer, *Hylotrupes bajulus*

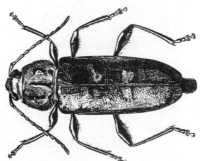

Black, with or without yellow cross stripes.                       428

428. (427) Somewhat flattened; blackish in color.                  429
Black with yellow cross stripes.                                   431

429. (428) Dull black with 2 divergent ivory white lines across
each elytron. Attack wood with bark and emerge from firewood.

*Phymatodes varius*

Similar in color, but lacking ivory white lines.                   430

430. (429) Dull black with bases of elytra reddish. Attack wood with bark and emerge from firewood.

*Phymatodes dimidiatus*

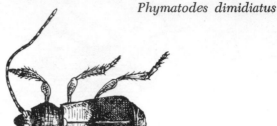

Dull black prothorax and elytra, head black.

*Phymatodes testaceous*

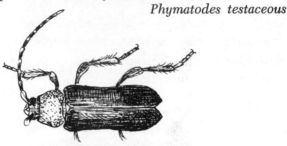

431. (428) Dull black with bright yellow transverse lines, zigzag across elytra, straight on prothorax, a distinct w-shaped yellow line near base on elytra; length 13-18 mm. Appear in fall. Emerge from firewood.

Locust borer, *Megacyllene robiniae*

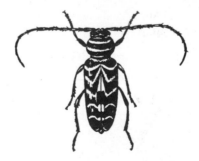

As above, except emerge in spring. Emerge from firewood.

Painted hickory borer, *Megacyllene caryae*

432. (385, 417, 1035) Hard with metallic luster; broad and flattened; antennae short, not clubbed (illust. 433).

Family BUPRESTIDAE:
FLAT HEADED WOOD BORERS    433

Moderately hard, not flattened beetles with metallic luster.    434

433. (432) Greenish blue elytra with copper colored margins; length 13-19 mm. Attack flooring and wood lacking paint or varnish.

Golden buprestid, *Buprestis aurulenta*

Flattened metallic colored beetles; length 6-35 mm. Usually emerge from firewood, sometimes furniture.

Other BUPRESTID BEETLES

434. (432) Front of head extended to form a snout; reddish brown to almost black; length 3-5 mm.

Family CURCULIONIDAE:
SNOUT BEETLES    435

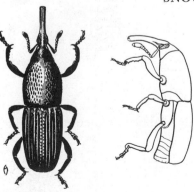

Front of head not forming a snout.                                  436

435. (434) Brown, subcylindrical; thorax as long as wide, densely punctate; feeble striae (lines) on elytra; length 2.5-3.2 mm. Attack soft wood lumber and woodwork.

Snout weevil, *Hexarthrum ulkei*

Not as above. Other wood-damaging snout beetles. Southern.

*Tomolips quericilia, Pissodes* spp.,
*Cossonus* spp., et al.

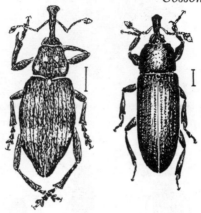

436. (434, 1038) Antennae filiform; spiderlike beetles; length 2-4 mm. Usually attacks stored foods rather than wood, sometimes wood.

Spider beetles, *Ptinus* spp.      517

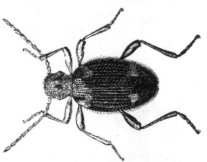

Antennae usually clubbed, sometimes sawlike or comblike.      437

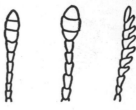

437. (436, 1032, 1038) Tibia with obsolete (reduced) spurs at tip; body nearly cylindrical; antennae with 3 segmented club, usually not sawlike or comblike; thorax largely covering head; length 3-8 mm. Attack old wood.

Family ANOBIIDAE     438

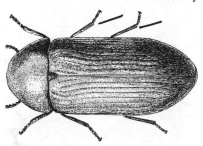

Tibia with distinct spurs at tip; antennae clubbed; reddish brown to black; thorax sometimes covering head; length 0.5-25 mm.     445

438. (437) Antennae serrate (sawlike) as well as clubbed (illust. 439).     439

    Antennae not serrate.     440

439. (438) Brown cylindrical, clothed with fine hairs; third ventral abdominal segment long, with basal process; antennae of male with serrations from the fourth segment on, or fitting close together; length 2-5 mm. Attack hard wood furniture and finish.

*Trypopitys punctatus* and RELATED SPECIES

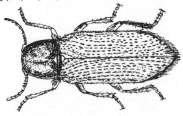

Brown to reddish brown, clothed with fine yellow hairs; antennae with segments III to X triangular; surface finely punctate (pitted); length 3.5-5 mm. Attack hard and soft wood and heart of soft wood.

*Xyletinus peltatus* and RELATED SPECIES

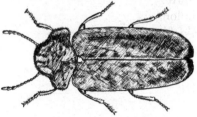

440. (438) Dark brown, subcylindrical with elytra mottled by patches of pale hairs; pronotum covers head; antennae 11 segmented; length 6-8.5 mm.

Death watch beetle, *Xestobium rufovillosum*

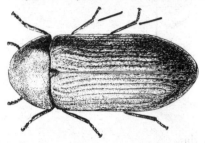

Not as above.                                                              441

441. (440) Reddish brown to dark brown with a fine covering of short yellowish gray hairs; prothorax raised strongly in middle, and overlapping head; elytra with longitudinal striae (fine lines), each with a row of closely set punctures (pits); length 2.5-6 mm. Eastern North America.

European furniture beetle, *Anobium punctatum*

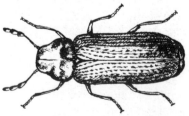

Not as above.                                                              442

442. (441) Reddish brown to dark brown; third ventral abdominal segment short; tibiae not produced externally at apex (tip) (illust. 443)

*Hadrobregmus* spp.       443

Not as above.                                    444

443. (442) Brown to dark brown, elongate, sides subparallel; pronutum convex and distinctly narrower than elytra; striae on elytra shallow, punctures regular; quite pubescent; antennae 11 segmented; length 4-6 mm. Pacific coast.

*Hadrobregmus gibbicollis*

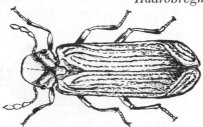

Reddish to dark brown, similar to above, but with 10 segmented antennae; length 3.5-6.5 mm. Eastern United States.

*Hadrobregmus carinatus*

444. (442) Reddish to dark brown, closely resembling *Hadrobregmus* spp., differing in that thorax is not margined and first and second abdominal segments are united; claws simple. Southern United States.

*Nicobium hirtum*

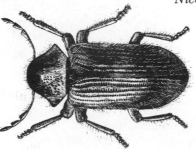

Differing from all of the above.

Other species of ANOBIIDAE

445. (415, 437) Antennae elbowed, with compact club, little longer than head; body short, compact, subcylindrical; dull brown to dark brown; tibia with a series of teeth externally, or a prominent curved spine at apex; length 0.5-5 mm.

Family SCOLYTIDAE: BARK BEETLES

Antennae not elbowed, club 2-3 segmented; length 3-25 mm.     446

446. (445, 1037) Slender, elongate, somewhat flattened, reddish brown to black; thorax not covering head; antennae with 2 segmented rounded club; first abdominal segment ventrally much longer than following segments; length 3-7 mm.

Family LYCTIDAE:
POWDER POST BEETLES    447

Cylindical; dark brown to black; thorax sometimes covering head; antennae with 3 segmented club; first abdominal segment, ventrally little longer than second segment; length 3-25 mm.

Family BOSTRICHIDAE:
FALSE POWDER POST BEETLES    452

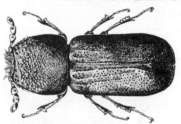

447. (446) Dark brown; prothorax in front narrower than base of elytra, the striae punctures in a double row; length 2.5-3 mm. California and Oregon.

Western lyctus, *Lyctus cavicollis*

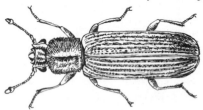

Brown to black; nearly always larger.    448

448. (447) Reddish brown with black head and prothorax; prothorax wider than long, widest in front of middle; hairs on elytra without definite arrangement; length 4-5 mm. Widespread, common in bamboo.

Brown powder-post beetle, *Lyctus brunneus*

Coloration not as above.                                                449

449. (448) Rusty brown; prothorax almost square, narrower than
     elytra; elytra with single rows of large, shallow, circular punc-
     tures, a deep elongate elliptical pit in middle of each elytron;
     hairs in longitudinal rows; length 3-7 mm. Widespread.

                                    European lyctus, *Lyctus linearis*

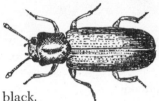

          Dark brown to black.                                          450

450. (449) Dark brown to black, with a broad white band near
     middle of elytra; elytra with rows of closely set punctures;
     lateral margins of thorax converge behind; yellow pubescence
     over body; length 4 mm.

                            White-marked powder-post beetle,
                     *Trogxylon* (*Lyctus*) *parallelopipedum*

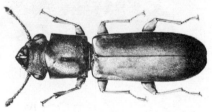

          Not as above.                                                 451

451. (450) Black, slender, somewhat flattened; prothorax usually
     with a broad, shallow median depression; elytra finely, deeply
     punctate in rows; length 5 mm., males much smaller. Southern
     half of United States.

                            Southern lyctus, *Lyctus planicollis*

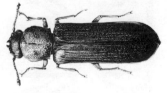

          Different from any of above.
                     Other powder post beetles, *Lyctus* spp. et al.

452. (446, 1038) Large, black; densely punctate on elytra, coarsely punctate on head and thorax; mandibles large and prominent; length 15-20 mm. Western United States.

*Polycaon stouti*

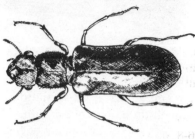

       Smaller beetles.                      453

453. (452) Brown, cylindrical; length 3-4 mm. Attack bamboo. Imported from Asia. (See 448, *L. brunneus*.)

*Dinoderus minutus*

       Not attacking bamboo.                 454

454. (453) Black, dull yellowish or reddish on basal third of elytra; thorax covering head; elytral declivity concave with 3 spines on each side; length 5-6 mm. Eastern North America.

Red-shouldered powder-post beetle,
*Xylobiops basilaris*

       Not as above.                       455

455. (454) Dark brown to black; thorax covering head, numerous tubercles on anterior half; elytra sloping sharply at posterior end, striae faint; length 5-6 mm.

Lead cable borer, *Scobiaca declivis*

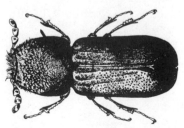

       Not as any of above.

Other false powder-post beeetles:
genera *Amphicerus, Stephanopachys* et al.

456. (379-416) Length of head, thorax and abdomen combined
more than 6 mm.                                                    457
    Length about 6 mm. or less.                                    474

457. (456) Elongate, rather flat; olive green with darker side
stripes on elytra; antennae filiform, about half as long as
body; length 6-8 mm. Hibernate in structures.
                     Elm leaf beetle, *Galerucella xanthomelaena*

    Not as above.                                                  458

458. (457) Rounded or hemispherical; generally red or yellow with
black spots, or black with white, yellow or red spots; antennae
short with a small distinct 3 segmented club; leaves yellow
stain on hands and fabrics if disturbed or crushed; length
8 mm. or less. Hibernate in structures.
            Family COCCINELLIDAE: LADY BEETLES

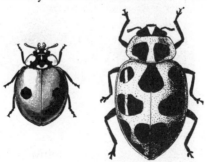

    Not as above.                                                  459

459. (458) Antennae filiform, or if enlarged, only slightly and
then only gradually, never clubbed.                                460

    Antennae distinctly clubbed.                                   464

460. (459) Elongate, brown to dark brown; prothorax loosely joined to mesothorax; prosternum with a spine which fits into a groove in mesosternum; capable of jumping when on back by bending prothorax backward to suddenly release the spine from the groove. Largely incidental in structures.

Family ELATERIDAE: CLICK BEETLES

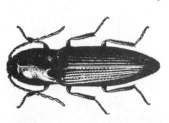 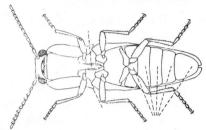

Lacking the ventral spine. 461

461. (460) Black; elongate; antennae slightly and gradually enlarged toward tip; front and middle tarsi 5 segmented, hind tarsi 4 segmented; length 12-20 mm. Attack cereals. 463

Generally dark, shiny; very active; antennae filiform; tarsi 5 segmented; variable in color and size. Incidental in structures, predaceous on insects.

Family CARABIDAE: GROUND BEETLES 462

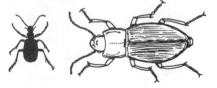

462. (461) Dark brown to black; small, 7 mm. A very repellent and disagreeable fetid odor emitted when disturbed. Western United States and Canada.

Stink beetle, *Nomius pygmaeus*

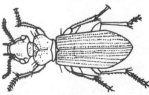

Lacking the extreme repellent and fetid odor.

Other GROUND BEETLES

463. (461) Black, sometimes dark brown; polished; prothorax finely punctured; elytra longitudinally striated or grooved; length 12-20 mm. More common in North.

Yellow mealworm, *Tenebrio molitor*

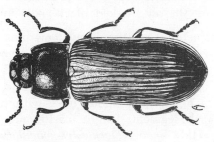

Dull black, sometimes very dark brown, lacking the polished surface; otherwise similar to above; length 12-20 mm. Widespread.

Dark mealworm, *Tenebrio obscurus*

464. (459, 1057) Head and thorax distinctly separated from abdomen and elytra by a deep notch on either side to produce a somewhat thread-waisted appearance; body noticeably flattened; length 8-12 mm. Attacks cereals.

Cadelle, *Tenebroides mauritanicus*

Thorax broadly joined to abdomen; length 6-11 mm. Attack animal products.

Family DERMESTIDAE: LARDER and HIDE BEETLES 465

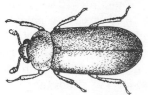

465. (464) Underside of abdomen white, or yellowish white (may be difficult to distinguish on greasy or oily specimens) with distinctly dark or black areas at sides (illust. 466).     466

Underside of abdomen more or less uniform brownish or black, never with sharply marked black spots in white area.     471

466. (465) Black, sometimes reddish brown; margins of pronotum light colored with white hairs; wing covers ending in tiny spines at inner margins; ventral abdomen with black spots at margins of each segment, last segment with large black central area in addition to marginal spots; male with pit and brush of hairs on fourth segment; length 5.5-10 mm. Widespread.

Hide beetle, *Dermestes maculatus* (*vulpinus*)

Not colored as above; elytra lacking tiny points.     467

467. (466) Black, shiny; ventral abdomen with large black areas on sides of basal 2/3 of segment I, smaller black areas on basal sides of segments II-V; males with dark pit and tufts of hair near center hind margin of segments III-IV; antennae reddish brown; pronotum bordered with whitish hairs; scutellum usually with brown or golden hairs; wing covers with whitish patches near base and sparse golden hairs, giving appearance of 4 transverse bands; length 6.5-8.5 mm. Widespread.

*Dermestes carnivorus*

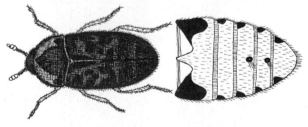

Ventral and dorsal patterns not as above.     468

468. (467) Black, shiny, sometimes dark reddish brown; ventral abdomen with large black areas on sides of basal 2/3 of segment I, smaller black or dark brown areas on basal sides of segments II-V, a large black or reddish brown area on middle hind margin of segment V; males with pit and tuft of hairs near middle of segment IV; pronotum with white or yellowish hairs forming a band on lateral and front margins; scutel-

lum with all hairs white to golden brown; wing covers with scattered white hairs among black hairs; length 6-10 mm. Widespread.

*Dermestes frischii*

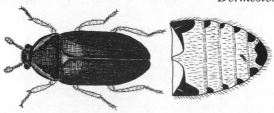

Ventral and dorsal patterns not as above.                    469

469. (468) Black, shiny; ventral abdomen with large side dark areas on basal 4/5 of segments I-IV, the fifth segment dark with basal white areas near sides; antennae and tarsi reddish; body brown above with pale or whitish patches; pronotum broadest in front of middle; length 9-12 mm. Western.

*Dermestes marmoratus*

Black, shiny; ventral abdomen with large black areas extending full width at sides of segment I, small black areas at sides of front half of segments II-IV, segment V largely black with 2 small white areas near sides.                    470

470. (469) Wing covers with numerous irregular patches of white hairs scattered among more numerous black hairs; inner (smaller) spur of middle and hind tibiae very much thickened and strongly curved; length 5-7 mm. Widespread.

*Dermestes undulatus*

Wing covers with patches of golden red hairs extending nearly to tip, and never with golden red hairs forming a more or less complete band at base; inner or smaller spur of hind tibiae not appreciably thickened and curved; length 5-7 mm. Widespread.

*Dermestes talpinus*

471. (465) Basal third of wing covers with a broad transverse whitish to yellowish band, with 6-8 black spots in the band; length 5-9 mm. Widespread.

Larder beetle, *Dermestes lardarius*

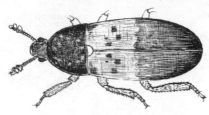

Lacking the whitish transverse band. 472

472. (471) Shiny reddish black to black above and below; wing covers feebly striated (fine lined); lateral line of first abdominal sternite very strongly incurved near base; male with median pit and brush on third and fourth sternites; length 7-9 mm. Widespread.

Black larder beetle, *Dermestes ater* (*cadaverinus*)

Shiny reddish black to black with striae and lateral line not as above. 473

473. (472) Wing covers distinctly striated; lateral line of first abdominal sternite distinctly turning outward (opposite of 472) near base instead of continuing parallel to outer segment margin; (metasternal epimeron hind margin feebly rounded, not sinuate); male with median puncture and brush on third and fourth sternites; length 7.5-9.5 mm. Widespread.

*Dermestes nidum*

Striae on wing covers indistinct or lacking; lateral line of first abdominal sternite parallel throughout to side of segment; (metasternal epimeron with hind portion distinctly and often strongly narrowed and hind margin distinctly and deeply sinuated); male with median pit and brush on fourth sternite; length 8-11 mm. Widespread.

*Dermestes peruvianus*

474. (456) Beetles with long snouts. 475

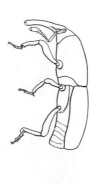

Beetles lacking long snouts. 480

475. (474) Attacking cereal and cereal products. 476
Not attacking cereal foods.
Family CURCULIONIDAE:
MISCELLANEOUS WEEVILS 479

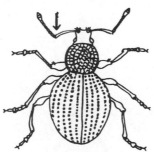

476. (475) Dark brown to black; with a short broad snout; length
3 mm. Attack soft or damaged cereals.
Broad-nosed grain weevil, *Caulophilus latinasus*

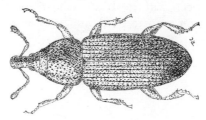

Reddish brown to black; with a long snout; about as wide
as above. 477

477. (476, 889) Black or dark red, lacking light spots on wing covers; length about 3.5 mm.

Granary weevil, *Sitophilus granarius*

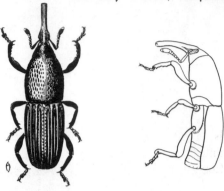

Black or reddish, usually with 4 obscure light spots on wing covers; length 2.3-3.3 mm. 478

478. (477) Length about 2.3-2.9 mm., width 0.82-0.92 mm. Prefers wheat, sorghum and rice, will feed on corn and other cereals. Widespread, more abundant in wheat storage areas.

Lesser rice weevil, *Sitophilus sasakii*

Length about 3-3.3 mm., width 1.07-1.15 mm. Prefers corn, sorghum and rice; will feed on wheat and other cereals; more abundant on corn in field and in storage. Widespread.

Rice weevil, *Sitophilus oryza*

479. (475) Black or dark brown, usually shiny; length 5-6 mm. Chance invaders in structures.

Strawberry root weevil, *Brachyrhinus ovatus* et al.

Gray weevils; length 5-6 mm. Feed on many weeds and herbaceous plants. Chance invaders in structures.

Longhorned weevil, *Calomycterus setarius* et al.

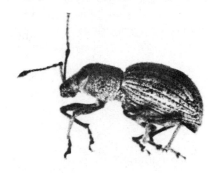

480. (474) Gray or grayish brown; wing covers shorter than abdomen, exposing at least the tip along the midline. Attack beans, peas, cowpeas, and similar products.                      481
    Not as above.                                                485

481. (480) Antennae serrate; 2 elevated ivorylike spots near base of wing covers; abdomen exposed at tip near middorsal line only; length about 3 mm. Attacks cowpeas in field, sometimes other beans and peas, emerge in storage and breed in storage. Southern.

Cowpea weevil, *Bruchus chinensis*

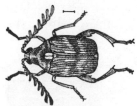

Antennae not serrate; abdomen exposed at tip for full width of body; length 3-5 mm. Attack beans and peas in storage.       482

482. (481) Brownish gray, with 4 dark spots on wing covers, 2 near tip and 2 near middle. Attack cowpeas, sometimes other peas and beans, emerge in storage and breed in storage. Southern.

Southern cowpea weevil, *Callosobruchus maculatus*

Lacking 4 dark spots on wing covers; antennae gradually enlarged toward tip, thus showing a slight club.　　483

483. (482) Gray to brownish gray; small distinct white spots above; length 4-5 mm. Attack peas in field, emerge in storage. One individual per pea; does not attack dry peas.

Pea weevil, *Bruchus pisorum*

Not as above; not common in peas.　　484

484. (483) Resembles above, but with fainter markings; prothorax somewhat narrower; length about 5 mm. Attacks broad beans, sometimes other beans and peas. Infests dry broad beans. Generally southern.

Broadbean weevil, *Bruchus rufimanus*

Olive gray to brownish gray; length 3-4.8 mm. Attacks a wide variety of beans and peas, fresh and dry. Widespread.

Bean weevil, *Acanthoscelides obtectus*

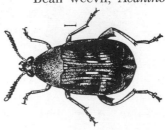

485. (398, 480) Pronotum and front fourth of wing covers red, head, antennae and underside black; length 4-5 mm. Attacks cured meats and cheeses. Southern.

Red-shouldered ham beetle, *Necrobia ruficollis*

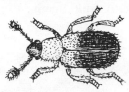

    Not as above.      486

486. (485) Pronotum and wing covers metallic blue or bluish green.      487
    Not as above.      488

487. (486) Legs reddish; length 3.5-6 mm. Attack cured meats and cheeses.

Red-legged ham beetle, *Necrobia rufipes*

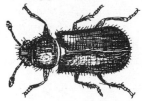

    Legs bluish green to black; length 3-4.5 mm.

*Necrobia violacea*

488. (486) Round or hemispherical; generally red or yellow with black spots, or black with white, yellow or red spots; antennae short with a small distinct 3 segmented club; leaves yellow stain on hands or fabrics if disturbed or crushed. Hibernate in structures.

Family COCCINELLIDAE: LADY BEETLES

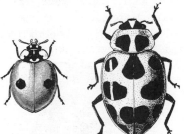

    Not as above.      489

489. (488) More or less shiny black.      490
    Yellow, reddish brown to dark brown, or dull black, sometimes mottled with white, yellow, brown or red scales or hairs dorsally.      499

490. (489) Hard, shiny, with short wing covers exposing about 1/3 of abdomen (2-3 segments); 2 paler spots on each wing cover, the larger area at tip; legs and antennae reddish; length 3-4 mm. Attack fresh and dried fruit.

Dried fruit beetle, *Carpophilus hemipterus*

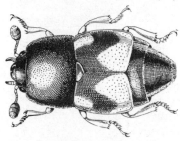

Not as above; attacks cereals and similar products and animal fibers as silk, wool, fur and feathers.    491

491. (490) Oval to oblong; black or largely black.    492
Elongate, flattened; black; antennae clubbed, the 3 segments about equal in length; front and middle tarsi 5 segmented, the hind tarsi 4 segmented.

Family TENEBRIONIDAE    496

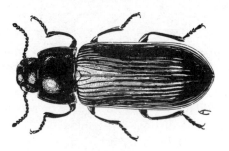

492. (491) Velvet black with purple tinge; reddish yellow antennae; length 5-6 mm. Infest damp cereals.

Red-horned grain beetle, *Platydema ruficorne*

493. (492) Shiny black; head folded under so it is not readily visible from above; antennae with third segment from tip as long as the preceding 6 combined; length 3 mm.

*Catorama tabaci*

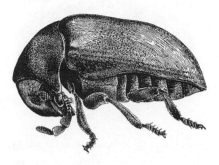

Dull brown to black; antennae clubbed. Attack cereals, wool, feathers, etc. 494

494. (493, 1058) Uniform dull black; last segment of antennae at least as wide and long as preceding 2 combined, in males much longer; length 2.8-5 mm.

Black carpet beetle, *Attagenus piceus*

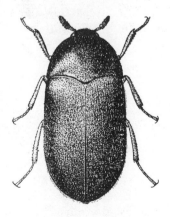

A band of brownish hairs or yellowish or white spots on wing covers. 495

495. (494) Dull black with a single transverse band of brownish hairs on basal third of wing covers; last segment of antennal club shorter than preceding 2 combined.

Carpet beetle, *Attagenus gloriosae*

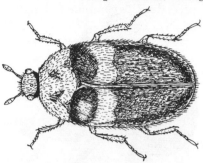

A whitish or yellowish spot near middle of each wing cover; last segment of antennal club long.

*Attagenus pellio*

496. (491) Shiny black above, reddish brown beneath; antennae and legs brownish; surface coarsely and profusely punctured (pitted); more elongate than oval.

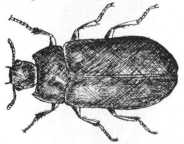

Black fungus beetle, *Alphitobius piceus*

Color beneath not as above.                    497

497. (496) Black to very dark reddish brown; sides of thorax nearly straight; surface finely and sparsely punctured; elongate; eye divided; length 5-6 mm. Live in damp cereals.

Lesser mealworm, *Alphitobius diaperinus*

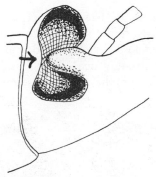

Black; closely resembling confused flour beetle.          498

498.  (497)  Black; length about 5 mm.

Black flour beetle, *Tribolium madens*

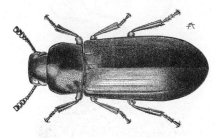

Black; length 6-7 mm.

False black flour beetle, *Aphanotus destructor*

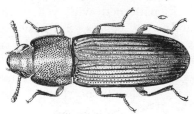

499.  (489)  Oblong to oval; often mottled dorsally with white, yellow, brown or red scales or scale-like hairs; antennae terminating in a loose to compact club.

Family DERMESTIDAE:

CABINET, KHAPRA and CARPET BEETLES    500

Not mottled with colored scales as above.          511

500.  (499)  Antennal club compact, composed of 3 segments.

CARPET BEETLES    501

Antennal club loose or less compact, usually composed of
more than 3 segments, sometimes 3 segmented; antennal cavity
at least partially enclosed; setae on dorsal surface somewhat
flattened, but not strongly scale-like; basal segment of hind
tarsus as long or longer than second segment, never shorter;
length 2-4.5 mm.                                                503

501. (500, 1058) Scales brick red along midline of wing covers;
length 2-3.75 mm.

Carpet beetle, *Anthrenus scrophulariae*

Lacking brick red scales along midline of wing covers.    502

502. (501) Body black, patterned with yellow and white scales
on pronotum and wing covers, 2 transverse zigzag bands
of white scales bordered by yellow scales on wing cover;
lower side of body covered with grayish yellow scales; posterior end of wing cover evenly rounded; length 1.8-3.2 mm.

Varied carpet beetle, *Anthrenus verbasci*

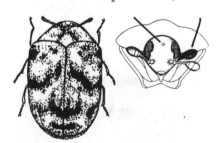

Body black, mottled with white, yellow and brown scales,
these areas outlined by yellow scales; lower side of body
pure white; posterior end of wing cover with shallow notch
at midline; length 2-3 mm.

Furniture carpet beetle, *Anthrenus flavipes* (vorax)

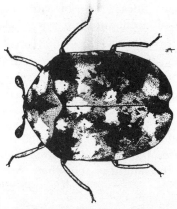

503. (500, 1057) Antennal cavity coarsely punctate (pitted), some of pits running together, punctures 2-3 times as large as eye facets; tergite (upper side of abdomen) of first periphallic (reproductive) segment forming an angle at middle of distal (back) margin; female antennal club 5-6 segmented.

*Trogoderma simplex*

Antennal cavity finely pitted, punctures about the size of eye facets, or shining and finely striated (lined); female antennal club 3-4 segmented.                                                    504

504. (503) Wing covers of 1 color, or vaguely mottled on shoulder and tips only, without a definite pattern.                              505

Bicolorous (2 colors), at least a pattern of bands near base, just before the middle, and near tip of wing covers.              506

505. (504) Antennae with 9-11 segments, male antennal club with 5 or less segments, female club with 3 segments; tergite of first periphallic segment almost straight at middle of distal margin.

Khapra beetle, *Trogoderma granarium*

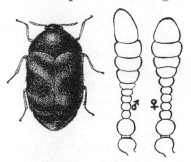

Male antennal club relatively compact and symmetrical; surface of antennal cavity smooth and shining, obscurely

175

marked with striae (lines); ratio of width across base of wing
covers to length of pronotum and wing covers ranging from
1:1.6-1:1.75.

*Trogoderma glabrum*

506. (504) Area of light maculation (spotting) of wing covers not
extending to base, but separated from base of wing cover
by at least twice the length of scutellum. Southwest and West.

*Trogoderma grassmani*

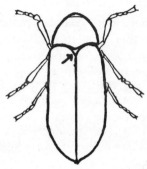

Light area extending to or practically to base of wing cover.    507

507. (506) Inner margin of eye distinctly emarginate; last (ninth)
abdominal segment of male flattened ventrally. Widespread.

Large cabinet beetle, *Trogoderma inclusum*

Inner margin of eye straight or nearly so.    508

508. (507) Male antennal club not serrate, more or less compactly
joined; wing covers with a light spotted (maculated) band
or loop near base, near middle, and near apex, without distinct longitudinal spotting connecting these bands.    509

Male antennal club distinctly serrate (illust. 510 upper),
loosely joined; basal and medial bands on wing covers connected by longitudinal spotting, sometimes broadly so.    510

509. (508) Light hairs on pronotum almost entirely golden yellow;
antennal club of male with 8 segments, ninth abdominal segment bluntly rounded at tip.

*Trogoderma parabile*

Light hairs of pronotum consisting of at least 1/3 white hairs; male antennal club 5-6 segmented, ninth abdominal segment sharply pointed at tip.

*Trogoderma teukton*

510. (508) Second to fourth antennal segments of male about equal in length and width, club pectinate (toothed on 1 side); the basal and medial spotting on wing covers sometimes running together, or connected by thin longitudinal lines of spotting.
Small cabinet beetle, *Trogoderma ornatum*

Third antennal segment of male minute, smaller than second or fourth, segments of club slightly pectinate (toothed); basal and medial light spotting often running together and extensive. Widespread.

*Trogoderma sternale*

 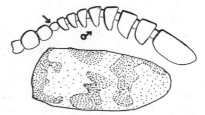

511. (499) Dark brown; with light colored, short, truncate (squared) wing covers, shorter than abdomen; antennae with tight club; length 2-3.5 mm.

Corn sap beetle, *Carpophilus dimidiatus*

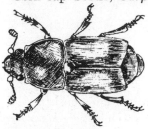

Lacking short, truncate wing covers.                              512

512. (393, 511). Reddish brown, shiny; body rounded (convex); Antennae 10 segmented, with compact club, which fits into a cavity in pronotum; abdomen with 5 free visible segments below.

Family MURMIDIIDAE: *Murmidius* spp.

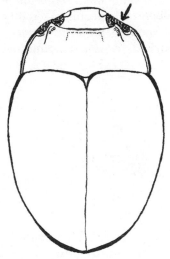

Not as above.                                                     513

513. (512) Slender, flattened; pale yellow brown; antennae loosely clubbed and smaller at tip; length 2-3 mm.

Long headed flour beetle, *Latheticus oryzae*

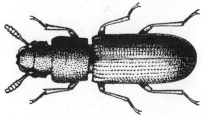

Reddish brown to dark brown.                                      514

514. (513) Females entirely wingless, resembling larvae, but with filiform 9 segmented antennae; males fully winged, with wing covers separated along midline for apical 2/3 of their length, exposing dorsal segments of abdomen; both with median ocelli; length 2-3 mm.

Odd beetle, *Thylodrias contractus*    381

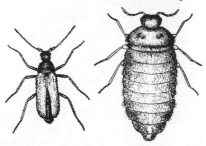

Not as above.    515

515. (514) Oval to globular, body about 1/2 as broad as long, or nearly so.    516

Elongate, body definitely less than 1/2 as broad as long.    528

516. (515) Dark reddish brown, subglobular, spiderlike; glossy smooth above, at least on abdomen; lacking color pattern; length 1.5-3.5 mm.    517

Reddish brown to dark brown, with or without color pattern, never glossy smooth above.    519

517. (436, 516) Abdomen, head and thorax smooth and glossy; length 1.7-3.2 mm.

Shiny spider beetle, *Gibbium psylloides*

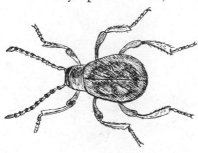

Head and thorax covered with scale-like hairs.    518

518. (517) Head and thorax densely covered with golden-yellow scale-like hairs; length 1.2-3.5 mm.

American spider beetle, *Mezium americanum*

Head and thorax densely covered with silvery scale-like hairs.

Northern spider beetle, *Mezium affine*

519. (395, 414, 516) Robust, oval; dark brown, clothed with mottled light and dark brown pubescence (fine hairs); antennae and legs reddish brown; antennae long, with loose 3 segmented club; length 3.5-5 mm. Attack stored cereals.

Coffee bean weevil, *Araecerus fasciculatus*

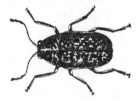

Not as above. 520

520. (519) Oblong, rounded; reddish brown; clothed with erect hairs; antennae with 3 segmented club, more compact than above; length 1.5-1.8 mm.

Hairy cellar beetle, *Mycetaea hirta*

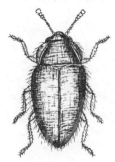

Not as above. 521

521. (520) Spiderlike, resembling small spiders or giant mites; with or without color pattern, often with yellow hairs; antennae filiform, longer than head and thorax, but never reaching tip of abdomen. 522

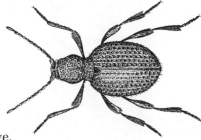

Not as above. 526

522. (521) Yellow hairs covering body, or at least wing covers. 523
Lacking yellow hairs, or inconspicuous, if present. 525

523. (522) Numerous long yellow silky hairs covering body; length 3-4.5 mm.

Golden spider beetle, *Niptus hololeucus*

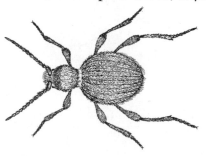

Lacking long silky hairs. 524

524. (523) Short yellow hairs over body; female with 2 white patches, anteriorly and posteriorly, on wing covers, which may join to form transverse bands across wing covers; male lacks white patches; female rounder and larger than male; length 2-4.3 mm. (see 525 also).

White marked spider beetle, *Ptinus fur*

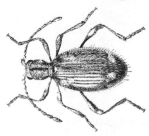

Short yellow or brown hairs on wing covers, lack color pattern and easily confused with male of *Ptinus fur;* length 2.5-4 mm.

Australian spider beetle, *Ptinus tectus*

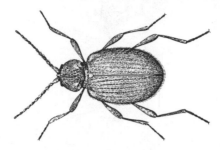

525. (522) Reddish brown with 2 irregular white patches, anteriorly and posteriorly, on wing covers with both sexes; lacking yellow hairs; length 2.2-4 mm.

Hairy spider beetle, *Ptinus villiger*

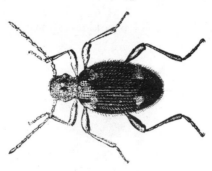

Uniform brown, without color pattern; female robust, male more slender; lack yellow hairs; length 2.3-3.2 mm. Easily confused with males of *Ptinus fur.*

Brown spider beetle, *Ptinus hirtellus*

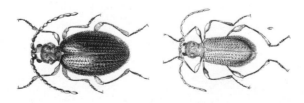

526. (521) Reddish brown, with 2 broad black bands across wing covers; length 3 mm.

Two-banded fungous beetle, *Alphitophagus bifasciatus*

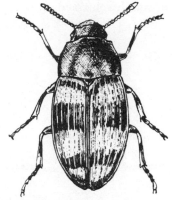

Lacking black bands.                                        527

527. (526) Robust, oval; light to reddish brown; head bent downward at nearly right angles to body, giving a humped appearance; lacking longitudinal striations on wing covers; antennae not clubbed; length 2-3 mm.

                        Cigarette beetle, *Lasioderma serricorne*

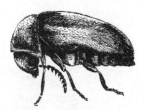

     Somewhat elongate; brown; head directed downward, but
not sufficient to give humped appearance; wing covers with
distinct longitudinal striations; antennae serrate (sawlike),
last 3 segments resembling a very loose 3 segmented club;
length 2-3 mm.

                        Drug-store beetle, *Stegobium paniceum*

 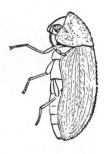

528. (515) Antennae distinctly clubbed.                                    529

Antennae not clubbed, but if larger at tip, only gradually
enlarged from base to tip and never a distinct club.              541

529. (528) Slender, cylindrical; dark brown, polished; head directed downward under thorax, not visible from above; length
3.2-4.2 mm.                                                                 530
    Elongate, flattened; head visible from above.              531

530. (529) Length about 3.2 mm., width about 0.8 mm.; wing
covers somewhat roughened by pits.
                Lesser grain borer, *Rhyzopertha dominica*

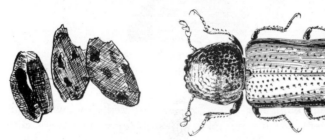

Length about 4.2 mm., width more than 1 mm.
            Large grain borer, *Prostephanus truncatus*

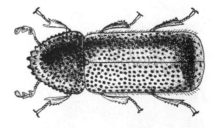

531. (529) Usually less than 3 mm. long, some up to 3 mm.        532
    Usually more than 3 mm. long, some only 3 mm.           537

532. (531) Reddish brown; flattened, elongate, margins of thorax and wing covers distinctly flattened; length about 2.5 mm.

Siamese grain beetle, *Lophocateres pusillus*

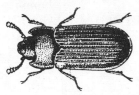

Lacking distinctly flattened margins of thorax and wing covers.                                                                    533

533. (532) Flattened, elongate; reddish brown, polished; prothorax nearly square with pointed corners slightly prolonged; length about 2.5 mm.

Square-necked grain beetle, *Cathartus quadricollis*

Elongate, somewhat rounded; reddish brown; prothorax usually wider than long, but some with prothorax longer than wide                                                                    534

534. (533) Projections at anterior corners of prothorax; not pubescent (hairy); less than 2.5 mm. Prefer damp cereals.

Foreign grain beetle, *Ahasverus advena*

Not as above.                                                                    535

535. (534) Oblong oval; hairy; prothorax with corners rounded; antennae distinctly clubbed (which separates it from drug store beetle, 527); length 2.2-3 mm.

Hairy fungus beetle, *Typhaea stercorea*

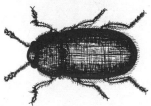

Not as above.                                                                    536

536. (535) Prothorax wider than long; length less than 3.5 mm.
Feed on fungi on cereals, paper, and other materials in damp
situations.

Families LATHRIDIIDAE,
CRYPTOPHAGIDAE: FUNGOUS BEETLES

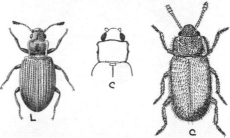

Prothorax longer than wide; length as above. Feed on
fungi as above in damp situations.

Some LATHRIDIIDAE

537. (531) Elongate; reddish brown; thorax and wing covers punctate; base of wing covers wider than prothorax, which is
rounded and narrow behind; length about 6 mm. Predatory
on cigarette beetle and other storage pests. Southern.

*Thaneroclerus girodi*

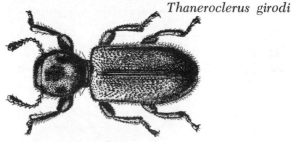

Smaller than above.                                              538

538. (407, 537) Elongate; polished dark brown; length about 4.8
mm.

Mexican grain beetle, *Pharaxonotha kirschi*    407

Elongate, somewhat flattened; reddish brown; length 3-4
mm.                                                             539

539. (538) Somewhat shiny, brown, with 4 paler spots on wing covers; length 3-4 mm. Feed on fungi on foods, paper, and other materials in damp situations.

Four-spotted fungous beetle,
*Mycetophagus quadriguttatus*

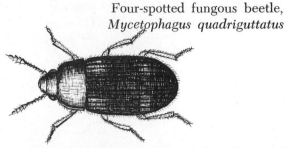

Brown, lacking paler spots; length 3.5 mm. Infest flour and other cereal foods. Widespread.

Flour beetles, *Tribolium* spp.     540

540. (539) Shiny reddish brown; antennae increase gradually from base to tip, but with a distinct 4 segmented club.

Confused flour beetle, *Tribolium confusum*

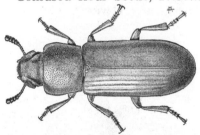

Shiny rust red; antennae with an abrupt 3 segmented club.

Red flour beetle, *Tribolium castaneum*

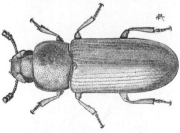

541. (528) Elongate, flat; brown; thorax with 6 saw-like teeth on each side; length 2.5 mm.

Saw-tooth grain beetle, *Oryzaephilus surinamensis*

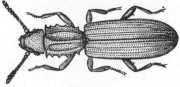

Teeth lacking on sides of thorax.                    542

542. (386, 541) Elongate; brown to dark brown; sometimes with yellow pubescence (fine hairs); wing covers very short, membranous wings beneath; curve tip of abdomen upward when disturbed; 6-7 visible abdominal segments ventrally. Scavengers, often in damp situation.

Family STAPHYLINIDAE:
ROVE BEETLES    386

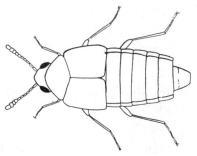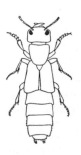

Lack the very short wing covers; otherwise lacking the combination of characters above.    543

543. (542) Elongate, flat; brown; less than 2.6 mm. long.    545
 Elongate; brown; about 3-4 mm. long, rarely as short as 2.6 mm.    544

544. (409, 543) Elongate, slender; dark brown to nearly black, frequently with conspicuous spots or bars on wing covers; head large; constricted at neck region; length 2.5-4 mm.

Family ANTHICIDAE:
*Notoxus, Anthicius* spp.

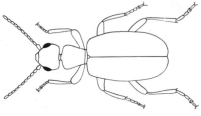

Not conspicuously narrowed at neck region.    549

545. (543) Reddish brown; antennae filiform, 1/2 as long as body or more; length about 2 mm.
  Flat grain beetles *Cryptolestes* (*Laemophloeus*) spp.    546

 Reddish brown; antennae shorter than head and thorax combined; length about 2 mm.

*Palorus* spp.    548

546. (545) Antennae of male as long as or longer than body, of female 2/3 length of body.

*Cryptolestes turcicus*

Antennae of both sexes from 1/2 to 2/3 length of body.    547

547. (546) Antennae of both sexes about 2/3 length of body.

Flat grain beetle, *Cryptolestes pusillus*

Antennae of male 1/2 length of body, of female 2/3 length of body.

Rusty grain beetle, *Cryptolestes ferrugineus*

548. (545) Elongate; somewhat rounded; shiny reddish brown; sides of front of head not extended backword so as to conceal a portion of eyes; length about 2-2.2 mm.

Small-eyed flour beetle, *Palorus ratzeburgi*

Similar to above, except sides of front of head strongly deflexed and extended backward so as to conceal front portion of eyes; length 2-2.5 mm.

Depressed flour beetle, *Palorus subdepressus*

549. (544) Robust, elongate; reddish brown; mandibles of male armed with a pair of broad, stout sharp incurved horns; length about 4.2 mm.

Broad-horned flour beetle, *Gnathocerus cornutus*

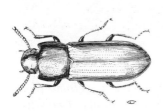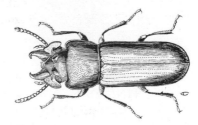

Similar, but smaller; mandibles of male armed with a pair of slender incurved horns, the tips nearly touching; length about 3.2 mm.

Slender horned flour beetle, *Gnathocerus maxillosus*

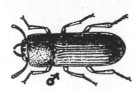

# LEPIDOPTERA (Moths)

557. (193) Both wings long and narrow; hind wing very narrow, with a fringe of long hair-like scales usually longer than width of wing membrane.
TINEIDAE, OECOPHORIDAE, GELECHIIDAE, and COSMOPTERYGIDAE    558

Wings broader, especially the hind wing which is broader than fore wing; fringe of hair-like scales usually shorter than width of wing membrane.
GALLERIIDAE: *Galleria, Achroia, Aphomia, Corcyra;*
PYRALIDIDAE: *Pyralis, Hypsopygia;* PHYCITIDAE: *Plodia, Anagasta, Ephestia;* NOLIDAE: *Celama*    570

558. (557) Fore wings conspicuously patterned.
TINEIDAE: *Nemapogon, Trichophaga, Setomorpha;*
OECOPHORIDAE: *Hofmannophila, Endrosis;*
COSMOPTERYGIDAE: *Pyroderces.*    559

Fore wings plain, concolorous (1 color), buff to blackish; not conspicuously patterned.

TINEIDAE: *Tinea, Tineola;*
GELECHIIDAE: *Sitotroga* (illust. 557 upper).    565

559. (558) Hind wings exceedingly long, narrow and pointed, with a wide fringe of hairs on both margins; fore wing long and narrow, creamy white mottled with brown; wing span 22-25 mm. Common in southern states.

Pink corn worm, *Pyroderces rileyi*

Hind wings not as above.    560

560. (559) Head and sometimes prothorax conspicuously white.    561
Head and shoulders not as above.    562

561. (560, 1048) Head white; basal third of fore wing dark brown to black, remainder of wing white mottled with black and gray; wing span 15-24 mm. South.

Carpet moth, *Trichophaga tapetzella*

Head and prothorax white in contrast with smoky to dark brown fore wings with paler blotches mixed with dark spots; hind wing narrow and pointed, with a very wide fringe; wing span 12-15 mm.

White-shouldered house moth,
*Endrosis sarcitrella* (*lacteela*)

562. (560) Buff to dark brown fore wings with 3 distinct black-ish brown spots and a series of dots along outer margin of wing; wing span 17-26 mm.

Brown house moth, *Hofmannophila pseudospretella*

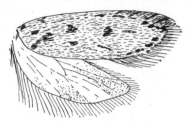

Pale yellowish to tawny, with spotted fore wings.                563

563. (562) Fore wings dull yellow to tawny, dotted with light gray bars. Southern states.

*Setomorpha insectella*

Fore wings creamy white, mottled with dark brown and spotted with black.                564

564. (563) Head pale, grayish behind antennae, dark brown mot-tling with dark spots on fore wing; wing span 9-16 mm. Wide-spread in northern states.

European grain moth, *Nemapogon (Tinea) granella*

Head yellow, blackish behind antennae, pale brown mottling contrasting with black spots; wing span 12-15 mm.

*Tinea cloacella*

565. (558) Hind wing elongate, the tip abruptly narrowed to front margin, fringe of hair-like scales about as wide as wing, whitish stripe running from base to beyond center of wing; front wing pale tan, narrow and long, nearly parallel sided, widest near base; wing span 12-15 mm.

Angoumois grain moth, *Sitotroga cerealella*

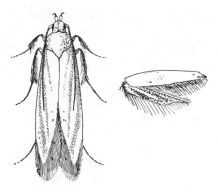

Both wings more rounded and less pointed, fore wing widest near center. 566

566. (565, 1048) Top of head with fluffy pompadour of reddish golden hairs; eyes black; body covered with golden shiny scales; antennae darker than body; wings nearly always lacking spots, or occasionally with a discal (center) spot; wing span 12-15 mm.

Webbing clothes moth, *Tineola bisselliella*

Indistinct spots, or fine blackish mottling on fore wings, sometimes generally blackish. 567

567. (566, 1047) Hind wing narrower than fore wing, the fringe wider than membrane; blackish in color. Southern Florida.
Plaster bagworm, *Tineola walsinghami*

Hind wing as broad as fore wing; head dull yellow to blackish; discal (center) spots distinct. 568

568. (567) Head dark with reddish tinge; antennae blackish; a transverse, dark band across front of thorax and basal half of tegulae extending along costa of fore wing a tenth of distance; fore wings finely mottled with dark, dorsal spots large and diffuse; wing span 11-17 mm. Northeast.
*Tinea fuscipunctella*

Head more yellowish; lacking transverse band across thorax. 569

569. (568, 1047) Eyes small, elliptical, separated by nearly twice their width; dull yellow, blackish on anterior thorax; fore wing heavily mottled with brownish concentrated toward center of wing, front fringe barred; wing span 12-13 mm.

*Tinea misella*

Eyes wider than space between them; head yellowish, antennae blackish; fore wing with darker scales toward tip, usually 3 center spots, small but distinct; wing span 10-15 mm. Widespread.

Casemaking clothes moth, *Tinea pellionella*

570. (557) Fore wing with 3 characteristic tufts of scales near front margin, the median tuft just beyond the middle and outer one near outer third; front margin brownish with interrupted white blotches, outer third with 2 more or less distinct yellow bands with associated brownish scales; hind margin with pale whitish hairs; hind wing largely white; length 12-16 mm. Southern.

Sorghum webworm, *Celama sorghiella*

Coloration not as above. 571

571. (570) Light dull rose color; fringe of both wings broad and pale yellow; pale yellow patches along front margin of front wing; hind wings crossed by 2 narrow yellow lines; wing span 13-20 mm.

Clover hayworm, *Hypsopygia costalis*

Lacking rose color; fringes never yellow 572

572. (571) Brownish moths. 573
    Grayish moths. 578

573. (572) Brownish; fore wings with chocolate brown at base and near tip; broad grayish white to olive brown center band margined on both sides with white; hind wings dark gray with 2 wavy transverse white lines; wing span 18-25 mm. Prefers damp cereals.

Meal moth, *Pyralis farinalis*

Lacking above colors. 574

574. (573) Large, yellowish brown, with a more or less distinct darker transverse line near tip of fore wing; female with large central black spot; male with 1 or 2 smaller black spots nearer front margin and a reddish yellow streak in center of fore wing; wing span 20-32 mm.

Seed moth, *Aphomia (Paralispa) gularis*

Not colored as above. 575

575. (574) Fore wing on outer 2/3 dark reddish brown to bronzy, inner 1/3 whitish gray, a dark brown line separating the areas; wing span 16-19 mm. Widespread.

Indian-meal moth, *Plodia interpunctella*

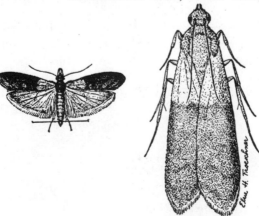

Color more grayish brown, if bronzy or coppery, not patterned as above. 576

576. (575) Smaller, pale, grayish brown; veins of fore wing slightly darkened; wings at rest tightly folded against body; length 12-14 mm.

Rice moth, *Corcyra cephalonica*

 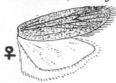

Larger, wing span 17-32 mm.; grayish brown, pale to dark; wings at rest tightly folded against body; run rapidly rather than fly when disturbed. 577

577. (576) Pale grayish brown; hind wing paler; with gray fringe; wing span, male about 17 mm., female about 21 mm.; infests dried fruits, beeswax in colonies and in storage.

Lesser wax moth, *Achroia grisella*

Usually dark grayish brown; hind 1/3 of front wing somewhat bronzy; hind wing paler with a dark line on fringe parallel to edge of wing; fore wing of male deeply notched; wing span 25-32 mm.; less if larvae have been starved.

Greater wax moth, *Galleria mellonella*

578. (572) Fore wings pale leaden gray with more or less distinct transverse wavy black bands; hind wing dirty white; moth at rest characteristically raises up on its fore legs giving a distinct slope to wings and antennae folded back against body; tip of abdomen turned up; wing span 20-25 mm. Widespread.

Mediterranean flour mouth, *Anagasta* (*Ephestia*) *kuhniella*

Gray moths lacking above characteristic pose when at rest. 579

579. (578) Gray to light grayish brown with 2 light colored transverse bands across fore wing, the inner band pale, bordered with black on outer margin, the outer band well defined, slightly wavy and bordered with thin dark lines on both sides; wing span 15-16 mm. Attacks tobacco and other products.

Tobacco moth, *Ephestia elutella*

Wings not banded as above. 580

580. (579) Gray moth with 2 transverse bands on fore wing, the inner band dark and nearly straight with a broad pale band on its inner margin; outer band pale and very wavy; wing span 20 mm.

Almond moth, *Ephesia cautella*

Gray moth; in flight vibrates wings rapidly and darts from place to place; wing span 14-20 mm.

Raisin moth, *Ephestia figulilella*

## HYMENOPTERA (Ants, Bees, Wasps)

587. (185, 198) First 1 or 2 segments of abdomen forming a slender pedical with knots, or knobs, on top, most conspicuous from a side view and strongly differentiated from remaining abdominal segments (gaster); antennae distinctly elbowed, with first segment (scape) very long.

FORMICIDAE: ANTS 601

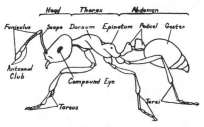

Pedicel not conspicuous, *or* if conspicuous, lacking knots, *or* if with knots, antennae never distinctly elbowed. 588

588. (587) Generally short and robust; usually with plumed or branched hairs for collecting pollen; hind tarsus broad and flattened, with hairs forming a pollen basket (A), or entire surface densely haired; long tongue (glossa) for sucking nectar; lacking yellow and black body pattern, *or* if present, pattern on hair only; frequently wax glands on under side of abdomen for nest building.

Families BOMBIDAE, APIDAE:
SOCIAL and SOLITARY BEES 590

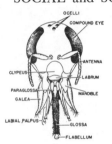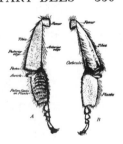

Generally more slender and elongate; less hairy, never with plumed or branching hairs; lacking broad flattened tarsus; mouthparts developed for chewing (illust. 589), not sucking; frequently with black and yellow body wall pattern, independent of hairs.

Social and solitary wasps:
HORNETS, YELLOW JACKETS 589

589. (588) Pronotum (p) touching tegulae (t); 2 terminal spurs on middle tibiae; eyes emarginate.

Family VESPIDAE 594

Pronotum not touching tegulae; petiole long and slender.

Family SPHECIDAE    598

590.  (588) Social bees; on or in structures, trees, etc., usually in crevices or in soil.    591

Solitary bees, or colonial at most, not social.    592

591.  (590) Large colonies; nests contain wax combs, in more or less vertical parallel rows, usually in cavities; workers attracted to exposed sweet materials; various shades of light brown to black; length 12-14 mm.

Honey bee, *Apis mellifera*

Small colonies; nest in cavities, usually in soil; wax combs irregular, with limited amounts of honey and pollen; bees large and robust, larger than honey bees; clothed with black and yellow hairs, sometimes with orange, red and white trimmings; may be attracted to sweets, if exposed.

Bumble bees, *Bombus* spp.

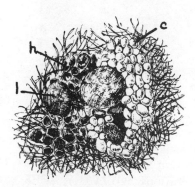

592. (590, 1028) Large and more robust than honey bees; resemble bumble bees, but distinguished by shining black, blue black, or wholly straw colored body; nest in dead wood of trees and structures, especially if weathered and unpainted.

Large carpenter bees, *Xylocopa* spp.: East, west to Kansas and Texas, *X virginica*, western United States and Lower California, *X. orpifex*, Southwest, *X. texana*, et al.

Smaller than honey bees; metallic and dark colored; frequently nest in nail or other holes, pithy stems, or rotten or soft wood.                                                                                          593

593. (592, 1027) Small, 5-8 mm. long; shiny, not hairy; bluish to metallic green; nest in hollow or pithy stems, or rotten wood.

Small carpenter bees, *Ceratina* spp.: *C. dupla, C. metallica, C. calcarata* et al.

Small, dark colored; often nest in nail or other small crevices in wood; seal nest with wax and other material.

Various SOLITARY BEES

594. (589, 948) Nests of paper made from wood fibers; established
social colonies; nests annual; queens hibernate; wasps black
with yellow or white markings *or* black, brown, or red with a
few yellow markings; length 13-25 mm. or more.               595

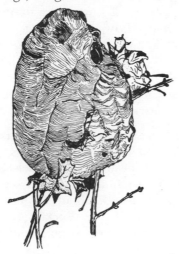

   Nests of mud, or other non-paper materials, often in holes
or crevices; wasps slender, black, brown and yellow, metallic,
steel blue, or shiny black.

                              SOLITARY WASPS     598

595. (594, 947) Nests in cavities or holes in ground, sometimes in
hollow stumps or logs near ground; attached above by a central

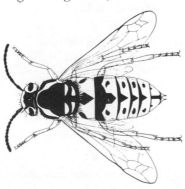

stalk (illust. 596); combs made from wood paper; colonies usually continue until fall; wasps black with yellow rings and markings; robust; length of males and workers about 13 mm., queens about 18-20 mm.

Yellow jackets, *Vespula* spp.: east of Rockies, *V. maculifrons*, West and Midwest, *V. vulgaris*, southern, north to Pennsylvania and Indiana, *V. squamosa*, West, *V. pennsylvanica*, et al

Nests attached above ground to bushes, trees, and structures; wasps black, brown or red with yellow and white or yellowish orange markings; length about 19 mm.    596

596. (595) Open paper nests of a single horizontal comb, attached by a central stalk to eaves, sheds, barns, in attics and on bushes, cells open downward; wasps black, brown or red with a few yellow markings; first abdominal segment narrow and somewhat elongated; length about 18 mm.

*Polistes* spp.: east of the Rockies, *P. annularis*, widespread, *P. fuscatus; Kappa* spp.: southern, *K. cubensis*, West, *K. flavitarsis*

Paper nests, suspended above ground, a series of horizontal combs enclosed in a globular envelope, up to several inches in diameter to huge nests (illust. 594 upper); wasps blackish or black with yellow and white, *or* yellowish orange markings; first abdominal segment broad; length 18-30 mm. or more.    597

597. (596) Nest up to several inches in diameter; gray in color; not fragile; wasps blackish or black with yellow and white, *or* yellowish orange markings; length *D. maculata* 22 mm., *D. arenaria* 15 mm. Widespread.

Bald faced hornets,

*Dolichovespula maculata, D. arenaria*, et al

Nests large, 10-18 inches wide, 1-3 feet long; many layers of combs, light brown to tan color; fragile; wasps with thorax and 1/3 of abdomen brown, hind 2/3 of abdomen yellow; large, 28-30 mm. North and East.

Giant hornet, *Vespa crabro*

598. (589, 594) Nests large and conspicuous, of mud, attached to rocks, trees, shrubs, and structures.    599

Nests in small holes or crevices sealed at surface, *or* small nests attached to bushes, *or* in soil.

Miscellaneous WASPS

599. (598) Nests are mud tubes attached lengthwise to structures, often several side by side and 3-6 inches long; tubes open at lower end; wasps shiny black, with white tarsi; length 18-25 mm. East of Rockies.

Organ-pipe mud dauber, *Trypoxylon politum*

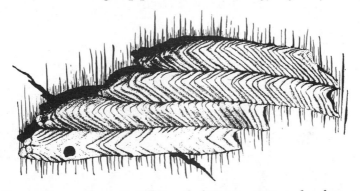

Nests are mud masses formed from a series of tubes on end built out about an inch from the attached surface, often more or less rectangular in shape; open outward; wasps steel blue *or* black and yellow; length 18-25 mm. (illust. 600).    600

600. (599) Steel blue in color, including wings; length 17-25 mm. Take over nests of S. *caementarium*. Widespread.

Blue mud dauber, *Chalybion californicum*

Black and yellow; length 18-25 mm. Widespread.

Black and yellow mud dauber,
*Sceliphron caementarium*

601. (587) Pedicel (waist) composed of 2 segments.

Subfamily MYRMICINAE    603

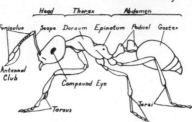

Pedicel composed of 1 segment (illust. 602).    602

602. (601) Lacking a conical spray nozzle on ventral tip of gaster (abdomen).

Subfamily DOLICHODERINAE    619

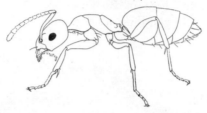

Under side of gaster at tip with a conical spray nozzle having a round opening, often surrounded by a circle of hairs.

Subfamily FORMICINAE    624

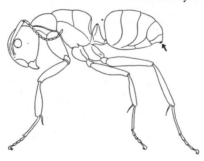

603. (601) Antennae 10 segmented, with 2 segmented club; hind margin of thorax above lacking spines.

*Solenopsis* spp.    604

Antennae more than 10 segmented, the club when present, usually having 3 segments.    608

604. (603) Workers extremely small, of one size, 1.5-1.8 mm. long; eyes exceedingly small; yellowish to light brown; shiny; males 3.5-3.6 mm., darker than queens; queens 4.2-4.8 mm. (a). Widespread, especially in East. (b) *Solenopsis molesta validiuscula.*

Thief ant, *Solenopsis molesta*

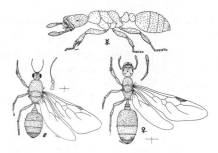

Generally large ants, workers quite variable in size, 1.6-6.3 mm.; eyes well developed. Can inflict painful stings.

Fire ants, *Solenopsis* spp.      605

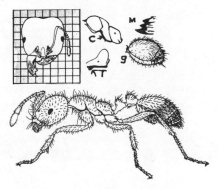

605. (604) Workers 1.6-5.8 mm.; yellowish brown, reddish brown to dark brown; queens up to 6.6 mm.      606

Workers somewhat larger, 2.4-6.3 mm.      607

606. (605) Workers yellowish red to dark reddish brown, last portion of gaster (g) brown to blackish; smaller workers darker than larger workers; carina (C) (ridge) on lower front margins of midthorax continuous and lacking teeth; front petiolar node in profile rounded on back side and with a ventral tooth

(T); biting edge of mandible (m) with 3 teeth. Southern, west to Arizona and California.

Native or southern fire ant, *Solenopsis xyloni*

Workers lighter in color than above; nearly or completely yellow. Arid regions, Texas to California.

California or western fire ant,
*Solenopsis aurea*

607. (605) Workers 2.4-6 mm.; brownish yellow to dark brown (var. *rufa* is more yellowish); carina (ridge) on lower front margin of midthorax with 1 or more teeth (T); front petiolar node (N) in profile forming a nearly straight line. Southern.

Tropical fire ant, *Solenopsis geminata*

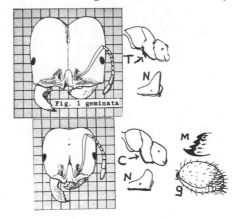

Workers 3.2-6.3 mm.; carina (C) on lower front margin of midthorax lacking teeth; front petiolar node (N) in profile rounded on back side; biting edge of mandible (M) with 4 teeth. Mounds conspicuous in pastures. Southern.

Imported fire ant, *Solenopsis saevissima*

608.  (603) Antennae of workers 11 segmented, male 12 segmented; a pair of spines on hind margin of thorax above.                                        609

Antennae 12 segmented, male 13 segmented; pair of spines (illust. 610) present or lacking.                                        611

609.  (608) Three or more pairs of spines on thorax above, including the pair on hind margin. Yard pest. Southern.

Texas leaf-cutting ant, *Atta texana*

A single pair of spines above, located on hind margin of thorax.                                        610

610.  (609) Tiny, workers of about 1 size, 1.5-2 mm.; usually yellowish; antennal club 2 or 3 segmented; move slowly; queens about 6 mm. Introduced, Florida and California.

Little fire ant, *Wasmannia auropunctata*
Larger, workers of 1 size, 3.2 mm.; petiole (waist) attached to dorsal surface of gaster; gaster heart-shaped from above, more convex below than above, coming to a point at tip; sting spatulate; light to dark reddish brown, with head and latter portion of gaster darker; wavy longitudinal lines on head and thorax. Widespread. Lined acrobat ant, *Cremato-gaster* spp. *C. lineolata* is the common species infesting structures.

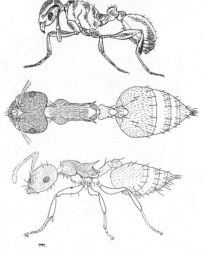

611. (608) Lower surface of head lacking a row of long, coarse hairs on either side. 612

Lower surface of head with a row of long, coarse hairs on either side. 615

612. (611) Ants with 2 distinct castes, workers and soldiers, differing greatly in size, the soldiers with large heads; antennal club 3 segmented. Warmer and arid regions. Occasional structural pests.

Big-headed ants, *Pheidole* spp.

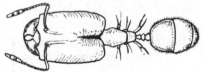

Ants with one distinct caste, workers of 1 size.

*Tetramorium* spp. 613

613. (612) Head lacking grooves (sulca) for antennae; basal half of first segment of gaster smooth and shining; head and thorax longitudinally striated (microscopic); light brown to blackish; antennal club indistinct, but 3 segmented; length 2.4-4 mm. Widespread, especially in East.

Pavement ant, *Tetramorium caespitum*

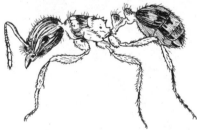

Head with grooves into which antennae may be folded. 614

614. (613) Hairs on head, thorax and petiole, erect and enlarged at tip; head longitudinally wrinkled (rugulose), the spaces

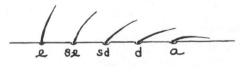

between wrinkles finely granular (granulose); length of workers 1.75-2.25 mm. Southern.

*Tetramorium simillimum*

Hairs and sculpture not as above; reddish yellow with gaster brownish to blackish; petiole as shown. Southern.

*Tetramorium guineense*

615. (611) Antennae not clubbed but funiculus gradually enlarged outward; red to dark brown; length 5-6 mm. or more. Yard ants, seldom invade structures. Gravel covered mounds 6-12 inches or more high, surrounded by a clear circular area. Pugnacious when disturbed. Southeast (1 species), Arid West and Southwest.

Harvester ants, *Pogonomyrmex* spp.: coastal Mississippi to North Carolina, Florida harvester ant, *P. badius;* British Columbia and South Dakota to Oklahoma and Arizona, western harvester ant, *P. occidentalis;* Southwest to California, red harvester ant, *P. barbatus.*

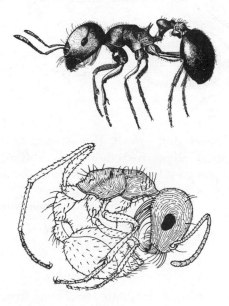

Antennae clubbed, club 3 segmented; smaller than above, less than 3.5 mm.

*Monomorium* spp.  616

616. (615) First 2 segments of antennal club about equal in length; workers about equal in size, but exhibit some dimorphism; about 2 mm. long. Southern.

*Monomorium destructor*

Three segments of antennal club successively longer; workers about equal in size, not at all dimorphic.  617

617. (616) Body shiny; uniform deep brown to black; anterior hump of petiole in profile about as high as long; length 1.5-2 mm. Widespread.

Little black ant, *Monomorium minimum*

Body only slightly or not at all shiny; yellowish to reddish brown. 618

618. (617) Body, except hind portion (gaster) dull in appearance (due to fine sculpturing); yellowish red to reddish, with at least the latter half blackish; workers (b) of nearly one size, slender, 1.5-2 mm. Widespread.

Pharaoh ant, *Monomorium pharaonis*

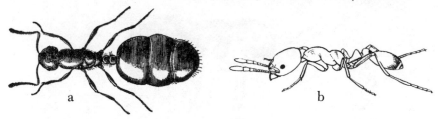

a                                          b

Head and gaster dull brown, thorax, petiolar humps, and appendages dirty yellow; front hump in profile shorter than base is long, the crest evenly convex from behind. Florida and Alabama.

*Monomorium floricola*

619. (602) Petiole (node) difficult to see, being strongly inclined or flattened, the abdomen (gaster) extending forward over the petiole (illust. 620); emitting a sweetish rotten coconut (terpenoid) odor when mashed.

*Tapinoma* spp. 620

Petiole more erect, not inclined or flattened, *or* hidden by gaster. 621

620. (619) Gaster white or pale whitish yellow, distinctly lighter than the deep brown head and thorax. Southern Florida.

Ghost ant, *Tapinoma melanocephala*

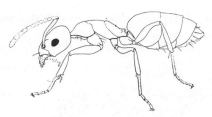

Uniform brown to black; workers 2.1-3.2 mm., queens 4 mm. Widespread.

Odorous house ant, *Tapinoma sessile*

621. (619) Posterior part of thorax with a pyramid-like (illust. 622) projection above; worker 1.5-2 mm. Southern and West Coast.

*Dorymyrmex* (*Conomyrma*) spp.   622

Pyramid-like projection lacking.   623

622. (621) Uniform dark brown.

Pyramid ant, *Dorymyrmex* (*Conomyrma*) *pyramicus*

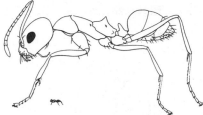

Dark brown with reddish tint on head and gaster.

Bicolored pyramid ant,
*Dorymyrmex* (*Conomyrma*) *bicolor*

623. (621) Workers 2.5-6 mm.; glistening velvet black abdomen (gaster), red thorax, and brownish black head; form files when traveling; queens up to 10 mm.

Velvety tree ant, *Liometopum apiculatum occidentale*

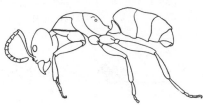

Workers smaller, 2.1-2.8 mm., largely of one size; uniform light to dark brown; musty odor when crushed; queens 4-6

mm., brownish. Maryland, Illinois, and California, much of South.

Argentine ant, *Iridomyrmex humilis*

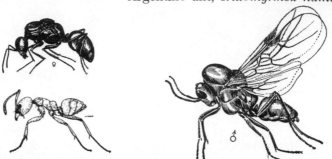

624. (602) Workers of each species of nearly one size, 5 mm. or less.      625

    Workers of each species variable in size, 3-13 mm.      637

625. (624) Workers robust, smooth and shining; uniform pellucid (translucent) yellow. Avoid light except when swarming. When crushed or disturbed emit a citronella odor. Often nest along foundations or basement floors; otherwise not structural pests.

Acanthomyops spp.      626

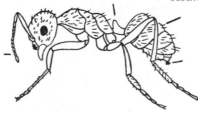

    Workers darker in color, not uniform yellow; 4 mm. or less. No distinct citronella odor.      629

626. (625) Antennal scape (illust. 627S) at rest extending beyond occipital margin of head more than thickness of tip of scape.      627

    Antennal scape at rest not extending beyond occipital margin of head, *or* at least not more than the thickness of tip of scape beyond the margin; fore femora with erect hairs on lateral (side) face as well as flexor surface.      628

627. (626) Crest of petiolar hump clothed with numerous close-set hairs (illust. 626), some arising from front face of hump, thus giving the upper part of hump a brush-like appearance.

Northern United States east of Rockies, south to North Carolina.

Acanthomyops murphyi

Crest of petiolar hump with a few erect hairs arranged in a single row along crest; erect body hairs long and coarse; gaster strongly shining; eye facets 6-9 in greatest diameter; length 4.2-5 mm. Coast to coast in northern United States, south to New Mexico and North Carolina; common in central and northeastern states.

Larger yellow ant, Acanthomyops interjectus

628. (626) Petiolar hump in profile with a blunt crest; from behind, crest is convex or flattened in the middle, but never deeply notched. Coast to coast in northern United States.

Acanthomyops latipes

Petiolar hump in profile with a thin, sharp crest; seen from behind the crest is deeply notched, or at least with a distinct impression. Northern United States west to Rockies and California, south to Tennessee and North Carolina.

Smaller yellow ant, Acanthomyops claviger

629. (625) Antennal scapes at rest never extending beyond occipital margin of head by an amount greater than the length of first funicular joint, often much shorter; erect body hairs short and golden, not course (illust. 632).

Lasius spp.    630

Antennal scapes at rest extending beyond occipital margin of head by at least 1/3 of their length, usually much longer; erect body hairs long, coarse, and usually brown or black.    633

630. (629) Workers ♀: maximum eye length (longest dimension) at least 0.20 times the head width; pronotal width of larger workers 0.57 mm. or more; smaller workers with 1 or more offset teeth (o) at basal angle of mandible. Queens: meta-

pleural (side of metathorax) gland with conspicuous guard hairs; from side view the scutum does not overhang the pronotum, but shares with it the anterior thoracic convexity; head width distinctly less than width of thorax just in front of tegulae; length of last segment of maxillary palpus more than 0.1 times the head width; at least 1, often 2-3 offset teeth (o) on basal angle and along basal border of mandible. *Males* ( ♂ ): metapleural gland with guard hairs; mandible (md) with distinctly preapical cleft (pc), basal angle (ba) often distinctly marked and clearly separating the masticatory (mb) (chewing) and basal border (ba); head width distinctly less than width of thorax just in front of tegulae; maxillary palp exceeding 0.10 mm. Southern Canada, northern United States south to Mexican border in Rockies.

*Lasius sitkaensis*

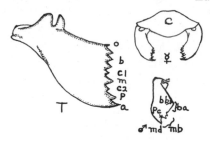

*Workers* ♀ : eye length exceeding 0.25 times the head width; posterior basal teeth (b) aligned with adjacent teeth of masticatory border (mb); color seldom yellowish brown, if so, scapes have erect hairs (illust. 631 e). *Queens*: metapleural gland, scutum, head width, and maxillary palp as above; posterior basal teeth (b) almost always aligned with adjacent teeth of masticatory border (mb). *Males* ( ♂ ): metapleural gland opening as above; mandible lacking a preapical cleft (pc), at the most the masticatory border (mb) feebly impressed in the middle; basal angle (ba) of mandible always broadly rounded, the masticatory border (mb) curving gradually into the basal border.

631

631. (630) *Workers* ♀ : with the majority the penultimate (next to last) basal tooth (illust. 630T, b) is markedly reduced in size, or the gap between the punultimate and terminal teeth is larger in area than the basal terminal tooth and variable in shape; scapes (illust. 601 upper) and tibiae bearing erect hairs (e); color light to medium brown, rarely dark brown. *Queens*: with penultimate basal tooth (illust. 630T, b) distinctly reduced in size relative to flanking teeth; scapes and tibiae with numerous erect hairs (e). *Males* ♂ : scape length

times 100/head width less than 80; erect hairs (e) common on scape (see *L. niger* below). Eastern United States, west to Idaho and New Mexico.

*Lasius neoniger*

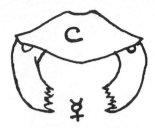

*Workers* ♀ : with penultimate (next to last) and terminal basal teeth (illust. 630T, b) subequal (about) in size, the gap between them with about the same area as the terminal tooth, and constant in shape. *Queens*: with penultimate basal tooth (illust. 630T, b) nearly always about same size as the 2 flanking teeth; scapes with or without erect hairs (e). *Males* ♂ : scape length as above; erect hairs (e) as above, *or* rare or absent on scape.

632

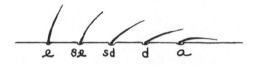

632. (631) *Workers* ♀ : pronotal width 0.53-70 mm.; scapes and tibiae with few or no erect hairs (illust. 631e). *Queens*: length of terminal segment of maxillary palp not exceeding 0.26 mm.; scape (illust. 601 upper) with few or no erect hairs (illust. 631e), no decumbent hairs (illust. 631d) outstanding above the pubescence. *Males* ♂ : erect hairs (illust. 631e) rare or absent on scape; subgenital plate (below genital organs) subquadrate (nearly square), the posterior border flat or weakly concave and the posterolateral (hind-side) flanges weakly developed or absent. Eastern half of the United States.

Cornfield ant, *Lasius alienus*

*Workers* ♀ : pronotal width as above; scapes and tibiae with numerous erect hairs (illust. 631e). *Queens*: maxillary palp as above; scape with numerous erect hairs (illust. 631e).

*Males* ♂: erect hairs on scape (see *L. neoniger* above).
Northwest, south to Arizona.

*Lasius niger*

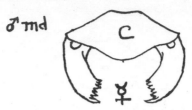

633. (629) Thorax from above with middle portion very strongly compressed; workers light to dark brown, shiny; abdomen (gaster) somewhat triangular; length 3-4 mm. Move slowly, forage in cool weather and at night. Concentrate on vegetable garbage; also peony bud secretions. Widespread.

Cool weather ant, *Prenolepis imparis*

Thorax from above with middle only slightly compressed (flattened from sides).

*Paratrechina* spp.    634

634. (633) Antennal scapes at least twice as long as head; antennae and legs remarkably long; body slender, with coarse erect (illust. 636) hairs; dark brown to blackish, with a metallic sheen or luster in certain light; length 3-3.5 mm. Movements rapid and apparently aimless. Widespread, but outdoors only in tropics.

Crazy ant, *Paratrechina longicornis*

Antennal scapes less than twice as long as head; body lacking metallic sheen or luster.    635

635. (634) Antennal scapes lacking erect hairs (illust. 636). East of Rockies.

*Paratrechina parvula*

Antennal scapes with at least a few erect hairs on anterior (front) surfaces, usually many erect hairs.    636

636. (635) Length 4-4.5 mm.; erect hairs on all surfaces of tibiae; pubescence (fine hairs) appressed (flattened against body) and prominent on head and gaster. Southern, common in greenhouses further north.

*Paratrechina fulva*

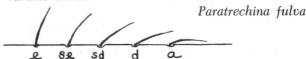

Length 3 mm. or less; erect hairs on tibiae mainly on extensor surfaces only; appressed pubescence on head and gaster absent or very obscure; antennal scapes with erect hairs abundant on sides and front; yellow to brown. Widespread, East of Rockies, *Paratrechina vividula* Florida and South Carolina, *Paratrechina bourbonica*

637. (624, 1025, 1039) Thorax in profile evenly rounded (convex), lacking a definite impression, *or* only very slightly impressed near middle of thorax above; hump of pedicel erect, sharp, hind margin with distinct backward slope, front margin much straighter; entirely black, *or* head and thorax yellowish to reddish brown and gaster black; length 3-13 mm. Live in wood above or below ground or in soil or under stones. Widespread.

Carpenter ants, *Camponotus* spp.    638

Thorax hollowed or concave above; hump on pedicel erect, sharp, with front and hind margins steeply or equally sloped; black, red, brown, or reddish brown; length 3-8 mm. Live in soil or rotten wood, often building conspicuous mounds of soil and plant fragments (illust. 650). Widespread.

*Formica* spp.    649

638. (637) Head of major worker not circular in cross-section; front of head not obliquely (slanting) truncate (squared), but more or less convex.                                                        639

Head circular in cross-section; front truncate. Not structural pests.

Other species of *Camponotus*

639. (638) Scapes of antennae, and legs with numerous long, coarse, brownish or golden erect (illust. 636) hairs on all surfaces; head and thorax yellowish red to red, gaster black; length of workers 4.7-9.5 mm. Southeastern United States.

Subgenus *Myrmothrix*
Florida carpenter ant,
*Camponotus abdominalis floridanus*

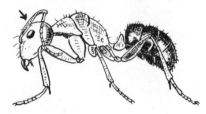

Erect hairs on scapes and legs, when present, fine, short and usually white, often confined to a row of bristles on flexor surface of legs.                                                             640

640. (639) Thorax of major workers longer than head (jaws extended); humeral (shoulder) angles of front of thorax much rounded; length of major workers usually less than 8 mm., at most 8 mm.

Subgenus *Myrmentoma*   642

Length and humeral angles of thorax as above; length of major workers usually more than 8 mm., rarely 8 mm. or less.   641

641. (640) Clypeus lacking or almost lacking a carina (ridge); antennal scapes never flattened at base; head of major workers (excluding jaws) at least as broad as long.

Subgenus *Camponotus*   643

Clypeus distinctly carinate; antennal scapes flattened at base; head of major workers as long as broad *or* distinctly longer than broad.

Subgenus *Tanaemyrmex*   647

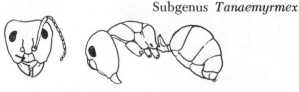

642. (640) Mid thoracic suture above not or scarcely impressed, so does not form a deep groove across thorax; scapes of antennae extending beyond the hind corners of head by at least as much as greatest thickness of scape; sides of face hairless; front (above eyes) feebly shining to opaque, the surface roughened by punctures and minute toothlike projections; sides of head of major workers moderately convex (rounded) and broad at level of jaws; middle of hind border of head straight or only feebly concave; color highly variable. Widespread from Ontario to Florida, west to Texas and North Dakota.

*Camponotus nearcticus*

As above except middle of hind border of head distinctly concave; head and thorax clear yellowish red or reddish, gaster black; workers 1.2 to about 8 mm. Common along Gulf Coast, west to Texas, north to Iowa.

Small carpenter ant, *Camponotus rasilis*

643. (641) Antennal scapes with numerous short, scattered erect hairs; entire insect shiny black, often with bluish reflections. British Columbia to Mexico.

Blue-black carpenter ant, *Camponotus laevigatus*

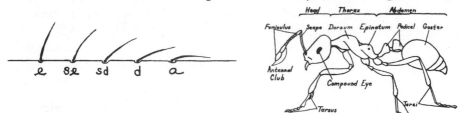

Antennal scapes with few or no erect hairs; color not as above, or if uniform black, not strongly shining.     644

644. (643) Antennal scapes of large workers reaching or barely extending beyond hind margin of head; pubescence on gaster less than half as long as erect hairs; head, thorax and gaster black, posterior portion of thorax often deep red, legs usually reddish or orange. Northern United States and Canada.

*Camponotus herculeanus*

Antennal scape extending beyond hind margin of head by at least more than the greatest diameter of scape.     645

645. (644) Pubescence on gaster absent, or very fine and sparse, entire surface of gaster shining; punctures on head coarse and conspicuous; head and gaster brownish black, thorax red. Nova Scotia to Virginia, west to Colorado and British Columbia.

*Camponotus noveboracensis*

Pubescence on gaster coarse and dense, about as long as erect hairs (illust. 643); surface of gaster dull except for a narrow band at hind margin of each segment.     646

646. (645) Head, thorax, petiole, and gaster dull black, pubescence pale yellow or white. Southern Canada to Florida, west to Texas and North Dakota.

Black carpenter ant, *Camponotus pennsylvanicus*

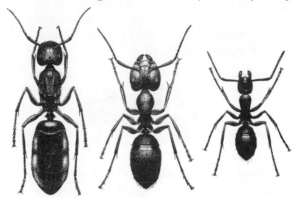

Posterior portion of thorax, petiole, and base of first gastric segment bright rusty (ferrugineus) red; pubescence golden yellow; workers, length 6.3-13 mm. New York to Georgia, West to Nebraska and Kansas.

Red carpenter ant, *Camponotus ferrugineus*

647. (641) Antennal scapes with numerous, fine, short, erect hairs; jaws with 5-6 teeth; length of major workers 12-14 mm. Arizona.

*Camponotus vafer*

Antennal scapes lacking erect hairs except for a cluster at tip; scapes of major workers extending beyond hind margin of head by an amount equal to or greater than length of first funicular joint.     648

648. (647) Antennal scape of majors distinctly flattened near head, with the flattened portion forming a small lateral lobe. Southern, Oklahoma and Texas west to California and Oregon.

*Camponotus maccooki*

Antennal scape of major worker flattened near head, but lacking a lateral lobe; hind corners and sides of head lacking erect hairs, sides of head feebly shining or dull, the punctures coarse and conspicuous; gaster not at all shiny. Western, British Columbia and South Dakota to Arizona and California.

*Camponotus vicinus*

649. (637) Second and third funicular segments of antennae together at least 1¼ times as long as first segment, and usually longer; anterior border of clypeus lacking a median groove, the margin evenly convex or angularly projecting in the middle, or rarely with fine irregular edge (serrations); antennal scape not longer than the distance from middle of clypeal border to middle of hind (occipital) margin of head, *or* if longer, the epinotum is distinctly angular and not excessively rounded above (illust. 637 lower).

*Formica* spp.    650

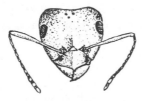

Not as above. Not structural pests.

Other *Formica* spp.

650. (649) Head of most workers, and especially large workers, with hind (occipital) margin very distinctly concave; pronotum in profile not evenly convex, but angular; few erect hairs on body; head and thorax reddish, gaster black; workers 3.2-6.3 mm. Nova Scotia to Georgia, west to Ontario, Wisconsin and Iowa; common in East. Mound builder and yard pest.

Allegheny mound ant, *Formica exsectoides*

Hind margin of head on small and medium workers at least, not all or only a trace concave, usually flat or slightly convex; pronotum in profile evenly convex, not angular.    651

651. (650) Head and thorax reddish, gaster brownish black; erect hairs on antennal scapes only at extreme tips, abundant on middle and hind tibiae usually on all surfaces, erect hairs on thorax somewhat unequal in length; head of large workers at least as broad as long, excluding jaws; head hairs somewhat less abundant and not much longer than those on thorax; length 3.8-8 mm. Alaska to Oregon, east to Manitoba and North Dakota, south to Colorado and Utah. Mound builder and yard pest.

Western thatching or mound ant,<br>
Formica obscuripes

Entire body nearly one color, *or* if 2 colored, thorax lighter than head and gaster; queens larger than largest workers, nearly 8 mm. or more, very smooth and shining; erect hairs, if present, on pronotum of worker never flattened or clubbed; front of head usually opaque, not shining.

Fusca group     652

652. (651) Antennal scapes and eyes covered with numerous, small erect hairs; rest of body with very abundant, somewhat coarser erect hairs. California, lower elevations. Infest houses.

Formica pilicornis

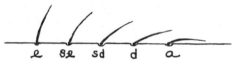

Scapes and eyes lacking erect hairs, except for 1 or 2 at tips of scapes; erect hairs, if present on rest of body, relatively sparse.

653

653. (652) Gula (under side of head) with at least 2 erect hairs; workers slightly variable in size, never greatly different in size; head longer than broad, excluding jaws; erect hairs on upper side of thorax and usually on crest of petiole as well; dark brown; workers 3-7 mm., females 8-10 mm. Western, east to Ohio. Yard and occasional house pests.

Prairie mound ant, Formica cinerea

Gula without erect hairs; punctures lacking, or only a few, immediately in front of eye, but with fine round punctures on surrounding area and raised roughness between punctures; side margins of eyes projecting beyond margin of head, when viewed from front of face; antennal scape of larger workers equal to or slightly longer than distance between middle of clypeal border and hind (occipital) margin of head; scape moderately curved and not much thickened at tip.

654

654. (653) Entire upper surface, except jaws, finely and densely roughened (granulose), completely opaque (not shining), even on hind edges of segments of gaster; head and thorax dull ferrugineus (rusty) red, gaster blackish brown; length 4-7.5 mm. California and Washington, low altitudes. Yard and occasional house pest.

*Formica rufibarbis*

Upper surface feebly to moderately shining, most of surface finely, not densely, roughened; upper side of first segment of gaster with erect (illust. 652) hairs scattered over entire surface; pubescence (fine hairs) of gaster usually sufficient to obscure surface; clypeal carina (ridge) from above sharp and distinct; color black with silvery pubescence on gaster. Southern Canada and northern United States, south to Florida and Texas. Disk nest, rarely a mound. Yard and occasional house pest.

*Formica fusca* et al.

## SIPHONAPTERA (Fleas)

The pest fleas can be identified to families in couplets 655-658, which lead into couplet 659. If you are not interested in family relationships, turn directly to couplet 659.

655. (182) Thorax greatly reduced, thoracic terga taken together shorter than first abdominal tergum; females sometimes with a reduced number of abdominal spiracles, (illust. 656); when gravid abdomen greatly distended.

Family Hectopsyllidae:
*Echidnophaga* and *Tunga* spp.    659

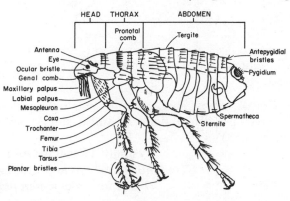

Thorax not greatly reduced, thoracic terga taken together longer than first abdominal tergum; gravid females, slightly, if at all enlarged. 656

656. (655) Typical abdominal terga each with but 1 transverse row of setae; frontal-epicranial groove usually absent; eyes usually present.

Family PULICIDAE:
*Cediopsylla, Ctenocephalides, Xenopsylla,*
and *Pulex* spp. 659

Typical abdominal terga each with more than 1 transverse row of setae; frontal-epicranial groove frequently present. 657

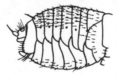

657. (656) Head usually elongated, always with 2 or 3 ventral flaps on each side adjacent to frontogenal angle; genal (illust. 658) comb consisting of 2 broad teeth on each side. Attack bats.

Family ISCHNOPSYLLIDAE

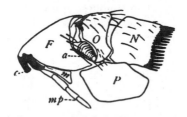

Head seldom elongated, ventral flaps absent. Do not attack bats. 658

658. (657) Genal combs absent; front not reduced; abdominal combs rarely present; abdominal apical spines rarely numerous (illust. 656).

Family DOLICHOPSYLLIDAE:
*Ctenophthalmus, Orchopeas, Nosopsyllus,*
*Diamanus,* and *Ceratophyllus* spp. 659

Genal combs present; front frequently reduced; abdominal combs frequently present; abdominal apical spines frequently numerous.

Family HYSTRICHOPSYLLIDAE:
*Epitedia, Stenoponia* and *Leptopsylla* spp.    659

Genal comb—      —Pronotal comb

659. (655, 656, 658) Combs lacking.        660

Combs present (illust. 658).        664

660. (659) Front of head angulate or with angulate tubercle; thorax above shorter than first abdominal segment above.        661

Front of head rounded; thorax not reduced, equal to or longer than first abdominal segment above.        662

661. (660) Hind coxae with a group of spinules on the inner side; length 1-1.5 mm. Attacks primarily poultry; also man, dogs, cats, rats, etc. Tropical and subtropical.

Sticktight flea, *Echidnophaga gallinacea*

Hind coxae lacking group of spinules on inner surface; length, not engorged, 1-1.2 mm. Tropical regions. Attacks man and many mammals.

Chigoe flea, *Tunga penetrans*

662. (660) One row of bristles on typical abdominal segment.　663

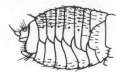 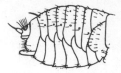

Two rows of bristles on typical abdominal segment. Southern United States. Rats.

Family MALACOPSYLLIDAE: *Polygenis gwyni*

663. (662) Mesopleuron divided by a vertical rodlike sclerotization; ocular bristle inserted in front of eye. Tropical and semitropical. Rats, also man.

Oriental rat flea, *Xenopsylla cheopis*

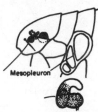

Mesopleuron not divided; ocular bristle inserted below eye. Cosmopolitan. Many hosts, often on swine.

Human flea, *Pulex irritans*

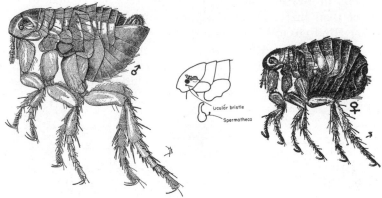

664. (659) Pronotal comb only.　665

More than 1 comb including genal and abdominal combs.　670

665. (664) One row of bristles on typical abdominal segment. Western United States. Rabbits and hares, also rats.

*Hoplopsyllus affinis*

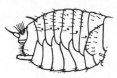

Two rows of bristles on typical abdominal segment.　　666

666. (665) Labial palps extending beyond trochanter of first pair of legs; second segment of hind tarsus with a spine longer than third segment and onto fourth segment. Western North America. Squirrels, also rats.

*Diamanus montanus*

TROCHANTER──────LABIAL PALP

Labial palps not extending beyond the trochanter of first pair of legs.　　667

667. (666) Fifth segment of hind tarsus with 4 pairs of lateral plantar bristles and 1 pair of ventral bristles near the base. East of Great Plains. Squirrels, also rats.

*Orchopeas howardi (wichhami)*

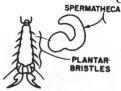

SPERMATHECA

PLANTAR BRISTLES

Fifth segment of hind tarsis with 5 pairs of lateral plantar bristles. Widespread in temperate regions and elsewhere. Rats.　　668

668. (667) Pronotal comb with 24 or more long black spines; front usually with 2 complete rows of lateral bristles, third row

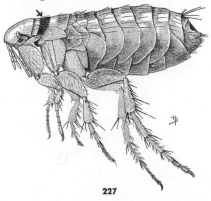

never complete; postantennal region of head with 2 lateral median setae. Preferred hosts: birds and fowls.

*Ceratophyllus* spp.   669

Pronotal comb with smaller number of spines, 18-20; front with 1 complete row of bristles; postantennal region with 1 row of setae. Rats, other rodents, also man. Widespread.

Northern rat flea, *Nosopsyllus fasciatus*

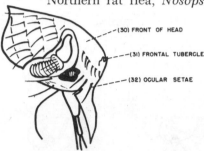

- - - (30) FRONT OF HEAD

- - - (31) FRONTAL TUBERCLE

- - - (32) OCULAR SETAE

669.  (668) Lateral row of 4-6 bristles on inner surface of hind femur (illust. 655 also); spermatheca and sternite VII as shown. Eastern North America. Fowls, birds, also cats, dogs, man.

European chicken flea, *Ceratophyllus gallinae*

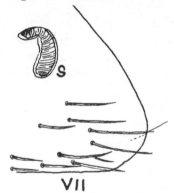

VII

Larger than above; spermatheca and sternite VII as shown. Western North America. Fowls, birds, also dogs, cats, man.

Western chicken flea, *Ceratophyllus niger*

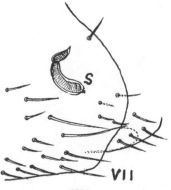

VII

670. (664) Three combs. Eastern United States. Field mice.
*Stenoponia americana*

Two combs, genal and pronotal.      671

671. (670) Genal comb with 2-4 spines; eyes reduced or absent.    672

Genal combs with 5 or more spines; eyes normal.      674

672. (671) Genal comb with 4 spines, pronotal comb with many spines; head apparently segmented. Coastal areas of North America. Rats and mice, also man.

Mouse flea, *Leptopsylla segnis*

Genal comb with 2 or 3 spines.      673

673. (672) Genal comb with 3 spines. Eastern United States. Rodents, man.

*Ctenophthalmus pseudagyrtes*

Genal comb with 2 spines. Eastern United States and Canada. Field mice and rats, house rats.

*Epitedia wenmanni*

674. (671) Genal comb spines blunt, directed more or less vertically. Eastern United States.

*Cediopsylla simplex*

Genal comb spines sharp, directed more or less horizontally; pronotal comb with 16 spines.      675

675. (674) Head length not twice the width; spine I of genal comb distinctly shorter than spine II. More or less cosmopolitan. Dogs, cats, etc., also man.

Dog flea, *Ctenocephalides canis*

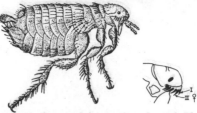

Head length twice the width; spines I and II of genal comb about equal in length. More or less cosmopolitan. Dogs, cats, rats, etc., also man.

Cat flea, *Ctenocephalides felis*

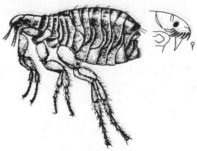

## DIPTERA (Flies)

685. (179, 191) Wings absent or much reduced; ticklike, or if wings well developed, coxae widely separated at base, the legs attached toward sides of thorax. Attack birds, bats, sheep.

Family HIPPOBOSCIDAE

Wings fully developed; not ticklike.                                    686

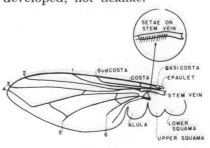

686. (685) Antennae with 5 or more free-moving segments. 687

Antennae with 3, some apparently 1 or 2, free-moving segments, the third often with rings or immovable segments (a); mesonotal suture incomplete or absent. 693

687. (686) Veins and margins of wings fringed with scales, or hair-like scales; 9 or more long veins or their branches reaching margin. 688

Veins lacking scales. 690

688. (687) Wings long and narrow with cross veins near the middle; veins scaled.

Family CULICIDAE: MOSQUITOES 728

Wings broadly oval, often pointed at tip, often held roof-like over body; body thickly covered with hair-like scales; wings lacking cross veins beyond basal third, veins hairy; length 1.5-2.5 mm.

Family PSYCHODIDAE 689

689.  (688) Second longitudinal vein bifurcated (2 branched) distant from base of wing; legs long and slender; eyes large and rounded; minute, 1.5-3.7 mm. Develop in damp situations. Females suck blood.

*Phlebotomus* spp.

Second longitudinal vein bifurcated near base of wing, wings at rest held roof-like over body; legs shorter; eyes smaller. Small flies associated with sewage and drains. Do not bite.

*Psychoda* spp.: MOTH or DRAIN FLIES

690.  (687) Ocelli (illust. 697) present; antennae inserted between the eyes, beadlike, long, many segmented; coxae much elongated. Associated with growing plants in structures.

Family MYCETOPHILIDAE:
FUNGOUS GNATS

Ocelli lacking.                                                                 691

691.  (690) Wings broad, front veins heavy, others weak; antennae bare, 10-11 segments, shorter than thorax; body short and stout.

Suck blood, serious pests outdoors, sometimes indoors.
Family SIMULIIDAE: BLACK FLIES
Wings longer and more narrow, back veins well developed.    692

692. (691) Delicate, slender, often confused with mosquitoes; thorax humped; wings long and slender; male antennae plumed. Develop in water. Attracted to lights, do not bite.
Family CHIRONOMIDAE: MIDGES

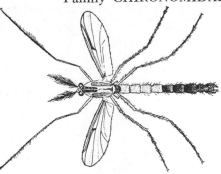

Minute, wings at rest held flat over back, often pictured, broad, costa ending before wing tip; male antennae plumed. Suck blood.

Family HELEIDAE (Ceratopogonidae):
BITING MIDGES

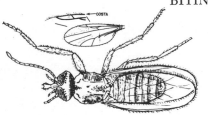

693. (686) Antennae 3 segmented, the third with rings or immovable segments, lacking an arista (long branching hair or bristle); discal (center) cell of wing twice as long as wide, 4-5 cells on posterior margin, 3A long, 3B ending behind tip of wing; squamae (reduced winglike structures beneath

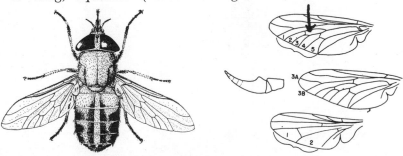

233

wings) (illust. 696) large; 2 spurs at tip of middle tibiae.
Suck blood.

Family TABANIDAE: HORSE FLIES

Antennae with 3, or apparently less, segments, usually an
arista on the third or last segment; wing with not more than
3 posterior cells. 694

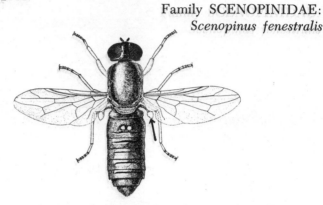

694. (693) Antennae 3 segmented, the first and second short, the
third lacking an arista or style; at rest the wings lie parallel,
one over the other, on the abdomen. Larvae are predaceous
on arthropods.

Family SCENOPINIDAE:
*Scenopinus fenestralis*

Antennae 3 segmented, the third with an arista (illust. 693
lower). 695

695. (694) Small "hunch-backed" flies; head small, palps large,
bristly; wings with 2 strong longitudinal veins and 4-5 less
distinct ones, cross veins lacking; antennae apparently 1 segmented, actually 3 segmented (A). Attracted to lights in
structures.

Family PHORIDAE

Wing veins not as above. 696

696. (695) Mesonotal suture incomplete or absent (B); second antennal segment lacking seam (A).      697

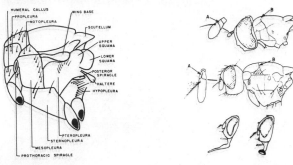

Usually large; squamae large; mesonotal suture complete (B); second antennal segment with seam (A); lapping or piercing mouthparts.      705

697. (696) Small, oral vibrissae usually present; vein above anterior cross vein unbranched (illust. 698); anal cell short or wanting; frontal lunule (f.l.) present; squamae (illust. 696) (scale-like lobe, usually white, beneath base of wing) small or absent.      698

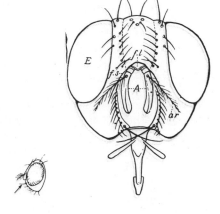

Usually larger or female with prominent ovipositor; oral vibrissae absent.      702

698. (697) Shiny reddish to black; costa unbroken; wings clear, often with dark spot near tip, anal cell present; top of head

convex; front leg usually much shorter than hind leg. Associated with decaying organic matter.

Family SEPSIDAE: *Sepsis violacea* et al.

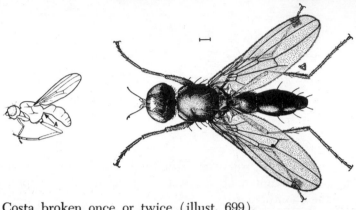

Costa broken once or twice (illust. 699).      699

699. (698) Costa broken twice, once near humeral cross vein, once close to end of vein I, posterior veins strong, with cross veins; antennae apparently 2 segmented, actually 3 segmented; palpi small.      700

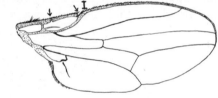

Costa broken once near end of vein I.      701

700. (699) First hind tarsal segment long and slender (B); mouthparts small (A); wing (illust. 699). Associated with fermenting fruit and organic matter.

Family DROSOPHILIDAE: FRUIT or VINEGAR FLIES

First hind tarsal segment broad (B); mouthparts thick and fleshy (A), wing as shown.

Family BORBORIDAE

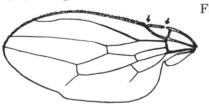

701. (699) Anal cell present; shiny black; top of head flattened; abdomen (A) broad basally; length 2.5-4 mm.

Family PIOPHILIDAE:
cheese skipper, *Piophila casei*

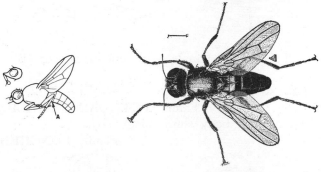

Anal cell absent (B); vein 5 (A) slightly irregular, not straight; smooth shiny, varied colors, including black; ocellar triangle large.

Family CHLOROPIDAE:
eye gnats, *Hippelates* spp.

702. (697) Spurious vein present (A); anal cell nearly reaching wing margin (B). Associated with fermenting organic matter, sewage.

Family SYRPHIDAE: DRONE FLIES

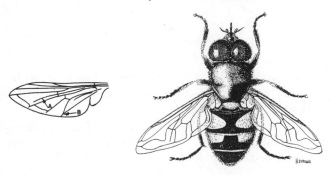

Spurious vein lacking; anal cell not nearly reaching margin of wing.

703

703. (702) Anal cell lacking.

Family EPHYDRIDAE

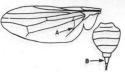

Anal cell short (A); female ovipositor prominent (B).                704

704. (703) Clypeus broad (a).

Family OTITIDAE (ORTALIDAE)

Clypeus narrow; body shiny black (b).

Family LONCHEIDAE

705. (696) Hypopleura bare, or with sparse fine hairs (a).

Family MUSCIDAE      707

Hypopleura with a row of strong bristles (b).                707      706

706. (705) Apical cell of wing strongly narrowed or closed at wing margin; only 2 notopleural hairs (a).

Family CALLIPHORIDAE:
BLOW or FLESH FLIES      707

Apical cell not strongly narrowed at wing margin (b).

Family MUSCIDAE (ANTHOMYIIDAE)      707

707. (705, 706) Body dull; gray or brown to black, or with abdomen blue or green; third long vein sometimes curved sharply forward near tip of wing.

Families MUSCIDAE and CALLIPHORIDAE      708

Body shining; metallic colored or black; third long vein always curved sharply forward near tip of wing.

Family CALLIPHORIDAE      719

708. (707) Thorax dull; abdomen blue or green.
    Family CALLIPHORIDAE    709
    Body dull; gray or brown to black.    710

709. (708) Squamae pale; abdomen strongly shining; scutellum
    (s) with 3 pairs of marginal bristles; postscutellum (ps) large,
    swollen.
    *Cynomyopsis cadaverina*

 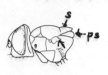

Squamae dark, with hind margin of lower lobe pale; scutellum (s) with 4-5 pairs of bristles; abdomen pollinose (whitish dusty appearance produced by microscopic hairs).
    Blue bottle flies: *Calliphora vomitoria,*
    *C. vicina* or other *Calliphora* spp.

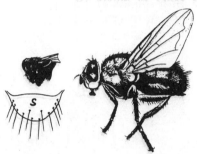

710. (708) Third long vein bent sharply forward near tip of wings
    so that it meets the margin close to second vein.    711

Third long vein somewhat curved, or straight.    714

711. (710) Thorax lacking distinct stripes, with short yellow hairs,
    hairy above; abdomen gray with irregular white patches;
    wings at rest overlap at tips. Odor of buckwheat honey when

crushed. Attics, wall spaces, around windows; enter for hibernation only.

Family CALLIPHORIDAE:
cluster fly, *Pollenia rudis*

Thorax with 3-4 distinct stripes. 712

712. (711) Thorax gray, with 3 black stripes; abdomen checkered gray, usually with 4 notopleural hairs.

Family CALLIPHORIDAE: *Sarcophaga* spp.

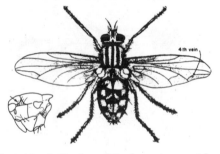

Thorax dark with 4 distinct black stripes; sides of abdomen often pale.

Family MUSCIDAE 713

713. (712) Flies collect and feed on food in structures; crawl on walls and furniture; rest on objects hanging from ceiling, especially at night; males with eyes closer together than with females, but much wider apart than *autumnalis;* frontal stripe broad and parallel-sided; females with abdomen usually yellowish on sides, at least toward base, rarely all gray black;

parafrontals (sides of front next to eyes) often yellowish tinted anteriorly, each about 1/3 as wide as median frontal stripe; length 4.75-8 mm. Breed in manure and fermenting organic matter.

House fly, *Musca domestica*

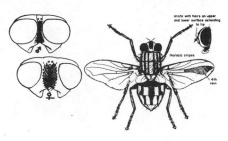

Flies do not collect and feed on food in structures, collect in attics and wall spaces for hibernation and around windows attempting to escape in fall and spring, and bright warm days in winter; males with eyes almost touching; abdomen above with second and third segments, except along median line, yellow to orange brown, remainder blackish; females with abdomen entirely dark in ground color, with strong gray and black pattern; parafrontals bright gray, wide, nearly as wide as frontal stripe; length 6 mm. Breed in fresh cow manure, collect on faces of cattle and feed on mucus membranes and exudates; pester other livestock and man also.

Face fly, *Musca autumnalis*

714. (710) Third long vein curved forward somewhat near tip.    715

Third long vein straight, or nearly so, not curved forward near tip.    717

715. (714) Proboscis (beak) elongate, stiff, blood sucking; thorax
with pale spot behind head. Breeds in decaying organic matter, enter structures.

Stable fly, *Stomoxys calcitrans*

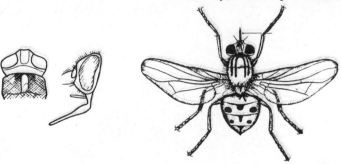

Proboscis enlarged and flattened at tip for lapping fluids;
tip of scutellum more or less pale.                               716

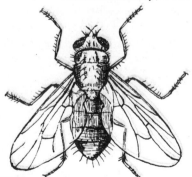

716. (715) Legs in part reddish brown.

False stable fly, *Muscina stabulans*

Legs wholly black.

*Muscina assimilis*

717. (714) First hind short vein reduced in length, not approach-
ing margin; flies often hover in air, seldom land on or feed
on food in structures; length 5-6 mm.

*Fannia* spp.   718

First hind short vein faintly continuing to margin of wing.

*Hylemyia* spp. et al.

718. (717) Head iridescent black, silvery white around eyes; antennae blackish gray; thorax blackish gray, with distinct longitudinal stripes, sides lighter, scutellum gray; large squamae white; halteres yellow. Breeds in manure, especially chicken, and decaying organic matter.

Little house fly, *Fannia canicularis*

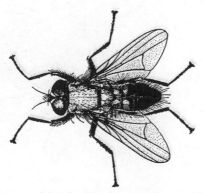

　　Head and thorax bluish black; antennae black; abdomen with dark median stripe, which, with segmentally arranged transverse bands, provides a series of triangular markings above; middle tibia with distinct tubercle. Breeds in manure and decaying organic matter.

Latrine fly, *Fannia scalaris*

719. (707) Head yellow below; thorax dark striped (illust. 720); anterior spiracle white (illust. 722).　　　　　720
　　Head dark below; thorax lacking stripes.　　　　　721

720. (719) Thoracic stripes of equal length; wing grayish brown at base.

Secondary screw-worm fly,
*Callitroga macellaria*

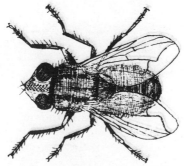

Middle thoracic stripe shorter than side stripes; wing yellowish brown at base.

Screw-worm fly, *Callitroga hominivorax*

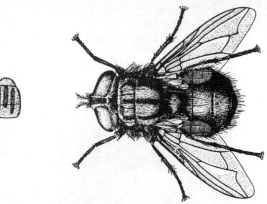

721. (719) Squamae uniformly dark.

*Protophormia terrae-novae*

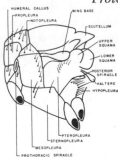

Squamae white or partially white. 722

722. (721) Anterior spiracle reddish; thoracic bristles reduced above.

Black blow fly, *Phormia regina*

Anterior spiracle blackish; thoracic bristles strong above. 723

723. (722) Abdomen pollinose (whitish dusting produced by microscopic hairs) above; males with squamae white; eyes moderately separated. 724

Abdomen strongly shining and not pollinose above; males with squamae partly darkened; eyes close together. 725

724. (723) Body usually green; male genital segments concealed; female lacking variegated pollinosity on abdomen below.

*Phaenicia sericata*

 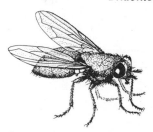

Body usually bronzy; male genital segments conspicuous, hairy; female with variegated pollinosity on abdomen below, readily visible when viewed in certain light.

*Phaenicia cuprina cuprina*

725. (723) Front margin of thorax entirely shining *or* with occasional traces of pollinosity. 726

Front margin of thorax uniformly pollinose. 727

726. (725) Antennae and palpi black or blackish.

*Bufolucilia silvarum*

Antennae and palpi reddish.

*Phaenicia caeruleiviridis*

727. (725) Antennae reddish.

*Phaenicia eximia*

Antennae black.

*Lucilia illustris*

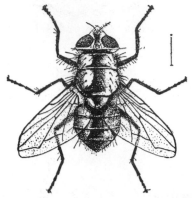

728. (688) Females with palpi about as long as proboscis, male with palpi clubbed; scutellum evenly rounded; when at rest, body at 45°-90° angle with resting surface; wings usually spotted.

Anopheline mosquitoes, *Anopheles* spp.  729

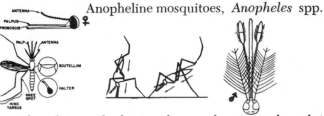

Female with palpi much shorter than proboscis, male palpi not clubbed; scutellum trilobed; when at rest, body at 15°-25° angle with resting surface.

CULICINE MOSQUITOES  740

729. (728) Wings with areas of white or yellow scales.  730

Wings with dark scales only, except occasionally for a silver or bronzy colored fringe at tip of wing.  734

730. (729) Two pale areas on front margin of wing.                   731

One pale area on front margin of wing at tip. Minor outdoor pests. Fresh water. Southeastern United States.
*Anopheles georgiana*, southeastern United States to Massachusetts and Canada, *Anopheles crucians*; brackish water, Atlantic and Gulf Coasts, *Anopheles bradleyi*

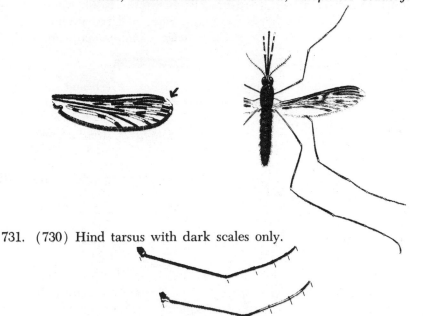

731. (730) Hind tarsus with dark scales only.                   732

Hind tarsus with broad white band. Fresh and brackish water. Structural pest, important malarial vector.
*Anopheles albimanus*

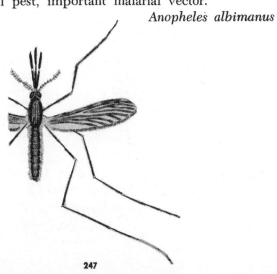

732. (731) Palp with white bands. 733

Palp uniform color. Widespread. Fresh water. Minor outdoor pest, minor malarial vector.

*Anopheles punctipennis*

733. (732) Terminal segment of palp entirely white. Fresh water. South and West. Structural pest, important malarial vector.

*Anopheles pseudopunctipennis*

Terminal segment of palp tipped with black. Fresh and salt water. Southwest and West. Pest of livestock and minor outdoor pest.

*Anopheles franciscanus*

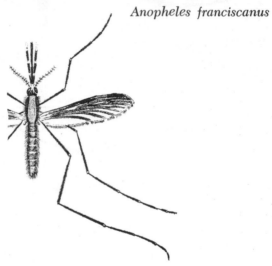

734. (729) Wings clear, lacking dark scales (a). 735

a                    b

Wings more or less distinctly spotted by clumping of dark scales (b). 736

735. (734) Thoracic bristles long, about 1/3 the width of thorax. Tree holes and artificial containers. Eastern United States to Nebraska and Texas. Important structural pest, minor malarial vector.

*Anopheles barberi*

Thoracic bristles shorter than 1/3 the width of thorax; if wings faintly spotted, then no evidence of light knee (illust. 728 upper) spots. Brackish pools and marshes. Atlantic and Gulf Coasts. Important outdoor pest.

*Anopheles atropos*

736. (734) Palp with narrow white bands; haltere knobs golden yellow. Fresh water. Eastern United States, Canada to Gulf Coast. Important structural pest, potential malarial vector.

*Anopheles walkeri*

Palps lacking bands; haltere knobs dark.                    737

737. (736) Tip of wing with a silver or copper colored fringe spot.    738
        Tip of wing lacking a pale (silvery or coppery) fringe spot.    739

738. (737) Scales on stem of second long vein, between the fork and dark spot, raised. Fresh water. Northern United States, Canada to Alaska. Structural pest.

*Anopheles earlei*

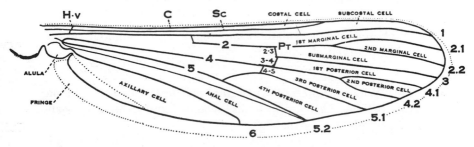

Scales on stem of second long vein, between stem and dark spot, rather closely appressed, not raised. Fresh water. West Coast. Minor outdoor pest.

*Anopheles occidentalis*

739. (737) West of Rockies into Canada. Fresh water. Important structural pest, malarial vector.

*Anopheles freeborni*

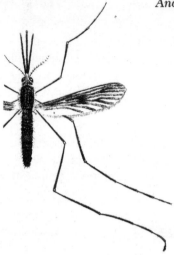

East of Rockies into Canada. Permanent fresh water. Important structural pest.

Common malaria mosquito,
*Anopheles quadrimaculatus*

740. (728) Proboscis stout toward basal half, outer half tapered and strongly curved downward. Develop in leaf bases of bromeliads, tree holes, and artificial containers. Tropical and semitropical. Not pests.

*Toxorhynchites* spp.

Proboscis slender, about same diameter throughout, never strongly curved downward. 741

741. (740) Wings with second marginal cell less than half as long as its petiole. Develop in pools, swamps, and along lake margins. Rarely bite man.

*Uranotaenia* spp.

Wings with second marginal cell at least as long as its petiole. 742

742. (741) Abdominal scales entirely dark dorsally, pale ventrally, with the 2 shades meeting laterally in a straight line; postnotum with a tuft of setae; wing squama and alula lacking a fringe of hairs. Develop in water in pitcher plant leaves, tree holes, etc. Seldom bite man.

*Wyeomyia* spp.

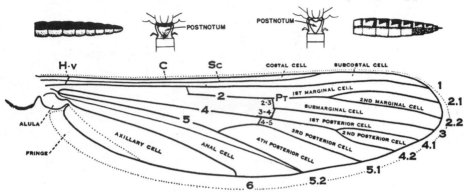

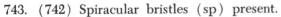

Abdomen above usually with pale bands or lateral spots; postnotum without setae; wing squama with a fringe of hairs    743

743. (742) Spiracular bristles (sp) present.    744

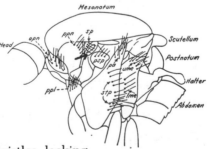

Spiracular bristles lacking.    745

744. (743) Postspiracular bristles (illust. 743 psp) present; tip of abdomen pointed; dorsal segments of abdomen with pale scales toward hind margin of segment, *or* if pale scales lacking, hind tibia with conspicuous long erect hairs.

*Psorophora* spp.    750

Postspiracular bristles lacking; tip of abdomen blunt; wings with cross veins nearly in a line.

*Culiseta* spp.    760

745. (743) Postspiracular bristles (illust. 743 psp) present.     746
    Postspiracular bristles lacking.                             747

746. (745) Wing scales very broad (illust. 749 upper), sometimes
    brown and white mixed; tip of abdomen blunt. Larvae and
    pupae attached to roots of plants, not free swimming.
                                                *Mansonia* spp.   764

    Wing scales narrow (illust. 749 lower), rarely moderately
broad; tip of abdomen pointed.
                                                *Aedes* spp.      766

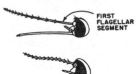

747. (745) Antennae much longer than proboscis; first flagellar
    segment longer than the next 3 combined. Gulf Coast. Occa-
    sionally bite man.
                                          *Deinocerites* spp.

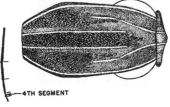

FIRST FLAGELLAR SEGMENT

    Antennae not longer than proboscis or only slightly so, first
flagellar segment about as long as each succeeding segment.       748

748. (747) Thorax bicolorous, with narrow longitudinal lines of
    white scales; next to last segment of front tarsus very short,
    only about as wide as long. Develop in water in plants, tree
    holes, and artificial containers. Widespread. Do not bite man.
                                          *Orthopodomyia* spp.

4TH SEGMENT

    Thorax unicolorous, lacking white longitudinal lines; next
to last segment of front tarsus much longer than wide.            749

749. (748) Wing scales very broad, white and brown mixed; fourth
    segment of fore tarsus longer than wide.
                                                *Mansonia* spp.   764

Wing scales narrow, uniformly dark.

*Culex* spp.    818

750. (744) Wing scales mixed dark and white (illust. 749 upper); hind femur with a more or less distinct subapical ring of white scales.    751

Wing scales all dark, *or* with only a few inconspicuous white scales on costal and subcostal veins; hind femur lacking subapical ring of white scales.    753

751. (750) First segment of hind tarsus with white rings at middle and base; wings speckled with brown and white scales in no definite pattern. Temporary pools. Widespread. Important livestock pest.

*Psorophora confinnis*

First segment of hind tarsus largely pale scaled; wings with definite areas of white and dark scales.    752

752. (751) Wing fringe of alternating groups of dark and pale scales; vein 6 white scaled toward end of wing. Temporary pools. Central United States to Mexico. Minor outdoor pest.

*Psorophora signipennis*

Wing fringe uniformly dark; vein 6 dark scaled near tip of wing, first vein with 2 pale areas. Temporary pools. Southern

United States, north to New Jersey, west to Nebraska. Important livestock pest.

*Psorophora discolor*

753. (750) Hind legs, including outer portion of femora with long erect hairs, very shaggy (illust. 754 also); last segment of tarsus never entirely white; very large species. 754

Hind legs not especially shaggy; ends of femora lacking erect scales; if tibia are somewhat shaggy, the last segment of hind tarsus is entirely white. Medium sized species. 755

754. (753) Thorax with narrow median longitudinal stripe of golden scales; proboscis yellow scaled on outer half, dark at tip. Temporary pools. East of Rockies. Outdoor pest.

*Psorophora ciliata*

Thorax lacking median longitudinal stripe of golden scales; proboscis entirely dark scaled; bluish cast. Temporary pools. Southeastern United States. Outdoor pest.

*Psorophora howardii*

755. (753) Hind tarsi entirely dark scaled; abdominal segments with apical, submedian triangular patches of golden scales toward tip. Temporary pools. Southeastern United States. Important outdoor pest.

*Psorophora cyanescens*

Hind tarsi with white near outer ends; abdominal segments with pale scales restricted to apicolateral (front and side) corners *or* to outer margin.                                    756

756. (755) Fourth segment of hind tarsus white scaled, at least on 1 side (illust. 757), last segment dark.                      757
Fourth and fifth segments and tip of third segment of hind tarsus white scaled.                                                 758

757. (756) Thorax with a broad longitudinal median stripe of dark scales, yellowish white scales laterally; hind tarsus with fourth segment white on 1 side. Temporary pools. Southern United States, north to New York, west to Texas. Important outdoor pest.

*Psorophora varipes*

Thorax clothed with yellowish white scales, lacking median longitudinal stripes of dark scales; fourth tarsal segment usually with basal 4/5 white. Temporary pools. Florida. Important outdoor pest.

*Psorophora johnstonii*

758. (756) Thorax clothed with mixed dark brown and yellow scales in no definite pattern. Temporary pools. Eastern United States, southeastern Canada. Important outdoor pest.

*Psorophora ferox*

Thorax with a broad median longitudinal stripe of dark bronzy brown scales, pale yellow or grayish white scales laterally (on sides).                                                759

759. (758) Pale knee spots present; palp less than 1/3 as long as proboscis; mesonotum with a broad median dark stripe. Tem-

porary pools. Southeastern United States, north to Pennsylvania, west to Nebraska. Outdoor pest.

*Psorophora horrida*

Lacking pale knee spots; palp a little more than 1/3 as long as proboscis. Temporary pools. Midwestern United States. Habits unknown.

*Psorophora longipalpus*

760. (744) Hind tarsi with pale rings, often very narrow, on some segments.                                        761

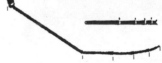

Hind tarsi entirely black.                                        763

761. (760) Hind tarsal rings broad, that of second segment covering 1/4-1/3 of segment; cross veins with scales.                                        762

Hind tarsal rings narrow, that of second segment covering about 1/10 of segment; cross veins lacking scales; wings with dense patches of dark scales. Fresh water. Western North America from southern California to Alaska. Outdoor pest, potential encephalitis vector.

*Culiseta particeps (incidens)*

762. (761) Femora each with a narrow subapical white-scaled ring. Fresh water. West Coast to Mexico. Outdoor pest.

*Culiseta maccrackenae*

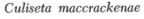

Femora lacking subapical white-scaled rings. Fresh water. West and north from Colorado to Alaska. Outdoor pest.

*Culiseta alaskaensis*

763. (760) Wing costa (c) and subcosta (sc) with mixed white and dark narrow scales, sparsely scaled. Fresh water. Wide-

spread.  Mexico to Alaska.  Important livestock pest, potential encephalitis vector.

*Culiseta inornata*

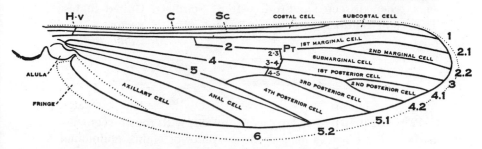

Wing costa entirely dark scaled; spiracular bristles (sp) yellow, not dark; points of origin of cross veins 3-4 and 4-5 separated by less than the length of either cross vein.  Fresh water.  Northern United States to Canada and Alaska.  Outdoor pest.

*Culiseta impatiens*

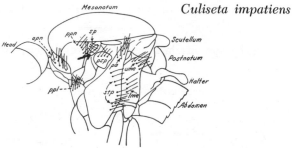

764.  (746, 749) Postspiracular bristles (illust. 763 psp) lacking; first segment of hind tarsus with median pale ring; proboscis pale near middle.  Fresh water.  United States, southern Canada.  Outdoor pest.

*Mansonia perturbans*

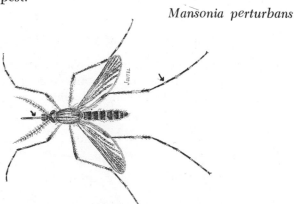

Postspiracular bristles present; first segment of hind tarsus lacking median pale ring.                                              765

765. (764) Palp a little more than 1/3 as long as proboscis, with fourth (end) segment about twice as long as third; spines of eight abdominal segment above clumped posteriorly (visible only when dissected). Fresh water. Southern United States. Important outdoor pest, potential encephalitis vector.

*Mansonia titillans*

Palp less than 1/3 as long as proboscis, with fourth segments about 1 1/2 times as long as third; spines of eighth abdominal segment above more or less uniformly spaced. Fresh water. Southeastern United States. Outdoor pest.

*Mansonia indubitans*

766. (746) Tarsal segments with white rings, at least on hind legs.    767

Tarsal segments lacking white rings, occasionally faint yellow rings.    790

767. (766) Tarsal segments white ringed on basal portion of segment only.    768

Tarsal segments white ringed near both ends, at least on some segments.    785

768. (767) Proboscis with white ring near middle.    769

Proboscis lacking white ring near middle.    772

769. (768) Abdomen with white to yellow dorsal median longitudinal stripe or a row of disconnected spots; wing scales either intermixed dark brown and white, or entirely dark.    770

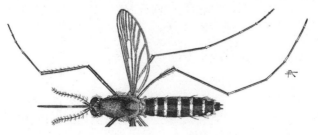

Abdomen with transverse basal bands of white scales, but lacking a median longitudinal stripe; wing scales entirely dark. Salt marshes. Atlantic and Gulf Coasts, Pacific Coast in California. Important pest.

*Aedes taeniorhynchus*

770. (769) Wing entirely dark scaled; first segment of hind tarsus lacking a median pale ring. Temporary pools. Southeastern United States to New York and New Mexico. Outdoor pest.

*Aedes mitchellae*

Wing with intermixed dark brown and white scales; first segment of hind tarsus with or lacking a pale median ring.    771

771. (770) Side (lateral) pale markings of abdomen white, the dorsal pale markings yellowish; first segment of hind tarsus with a definite yellow median ring; last segment of hind tarsus largely white. Salt marshes. Atlantic and Gulf Coasts from New Jersey to Texas. Important pest.

Salt marsh mosquito, *Aedes sollicitans*

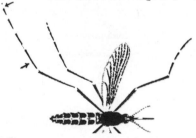

Lateral and dorsal pale markings of abdomen yellowish; first segment of hind tarsus variably marked, if a median pale ring present, it is white, not yellow; last segment of hind tarsus white basally, dark apically, rarely all white; palpi all dark. Temporary pools. Central and western United States, southern Canada. Outdoor pest.

*Aedes nigromaculis*

772. (768) Thorax with a conspicuous lyre-shaped marking of silver white scales against a dark background. Artificial containers. Southern. Important structural pest.

Yellow fever mosquito, *Aedes aegypti*

Thorax without such markings. 773

773. (772) Hind femora entirely pale on all aspects of basal half. Tree holes. Southwestern United States. Important outdoor pest.

*Aedes zoosophus*

Hind femora with basal half of anterior surface all dark *or* with intermixed dark and pale scales. 774

774. (773) Basal white rings of tarsal segments broad, especially on hind legs. 775

Basal white rings of tarsal segments narrow. 784

775. (774) Wing scales very large, broad, triangular-shaped, with dark and pale scales rather evenly intermixed. 776

Wing scales moderate in size, narrow, ligulate (long and narrow), with dark and white scales unevenly distributed *or* with pale scales absent. 777

776. (775) Proboscis with many pale scales intermixed to near apex (end); thorax with a broad median brown stripe; sides of thorax with mottled areas of brown and yellowish white scales,

the yellowish white scales predominating. Salt marshes. California. Important pest.

California salt marsh mosquito, *Aedes squamiger*

Proboscis with a few scattered pale scales on basal half; thorax with broad median dark brown stripe becoming golden brown anteriorly; sides of thorax white. Temporary pools. Eastern United States. Habits uncertain.

*Aedes grossbecki*

777. (775) Palp (illust. 728) all dark; abdominal tergites basally, laterally, and medially yellowish scaled, nearly surrounding large patches of dark scales, the median pale scales forming a longitudinal stripe. Temporary pools. Central and western United States, southern Canada. Outdoor pest.

*Aedes nigromaculis*

Palpi with some pale scales; pale scales of abdominal tergites never forming a distinct and complete median longitudinal line.                                                              778

778. (777) Abdominal tergites clothed with yellow scales, without basal bands. Temporary pools. Northern United States, Canada, Alaska. Outdoor pest.

*Aedes flavescens*

Abdominal tergites dark scaled, with pale basal bands, the dark scaled areas with a few to many pale scales in some places.                                                              779

779. (778) Tarsal claws with main tooth abruptly bent near base of lateral tooth, main tooth and lateral tooth parallel with each other. Temporary pools. Northern forests. Important outdoor pest.

*Aedes excrucians*

Tarsal claws with the main tooth bent beyond the base of lateral tooth (illust. 780). 780

780. (779) Tarsal claws with lateral tooth short and blunt, less than 1/2 as long as the main tooth, the main tooth bent before tip. Temporary pools. Northern United States, Canada. Outdoor pest.

*Aedes riparius*

Tarsal claws with lateral tooth long and slender, about 1/2 as long as main tooth, the main tooth bent beyond the base of lateral tooth. 781

781. (780) Lower mesepimeral bristles (lme) absent. Temporary pools. Northern forests. Important outdoor pest.

*Aedes fitchii*

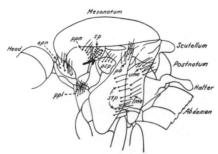

Lower mesepimeral bristles present. 782

782. (781) Tori (large globular segment at base of antennae) without white scales on dorsal surface; palps lacking hairs on

basal half of apical segment at inner ventral surface. Temporary pools. Western United States, southwestern Canada. Important outdoor pest.

*Aedes increpitus*

Tori with white scales on dorsal surface or with apical segment of palps bearing many long hairs on inner ventral edge, or with both.  783

783. (782) Lower mesepimeral bristles (illust. 781 lme) rarely more than 2; tori (illust. 781) with white scales on dorsal half. Temporary pools. Northern forests. Important outdoor pest.

*Aedes fitchii*

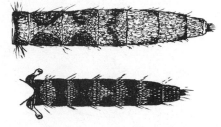

Lower mesepimeral bristles usually 3 or more; tori with or without white scales on dorsal surface. Temporary pools. Northern United States to Alaska. Important outdoor pest.

*Aedes stimulans*

784. (774) Lower mesepimeral bristles (illust. 781 lme) absent; seventh abdominal tergite mostly dark scaled, with white scales at apex of segment when present. Temporary pools. Widespread. Important structural pest.

*Aedes Vexans*

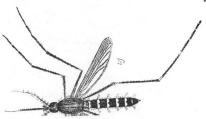

Lower mesepimeral bristles present; seventh abdominal tergite entirely pale scaled. Fresh and salt water. Coastal, northeastern United States, southeastern Canada. Structural pest.

Brown salt marsh mosquito, *Aedes cantator*

785. (767) Wing with white and dark scales intermixed.          786

Wing with scales all dark *or* with some white scales on anterior veins.          787

786. (785) Wing with dark and white scales evenly intermixed, the white scales predominating; accessory tooth of tarsal claw long. Temporary pools. Western Plains of United States, Canada, Alaska. Structural pest.

*Aedes campestris*

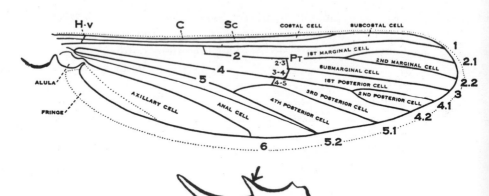

Wing with white and dark scales not evenly intermixed, vein 3 with more dark scales than veins 2 and 4; accessory tooth of tarsal claw short. Temporary pools. Northern United States, Canada. Important outdoor pest, potential encephalitis vector.

*Aedes dorsalis*

787. (785) Wing with a patch of white scales at base of costa (first vein).                                    788

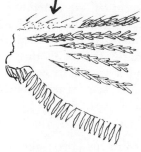

Wing with base of costa dark scaled.                              789

788. (787) Palps with white bands; scutellum with broad white scales. Tree holes. Western United States, southwestern Canada. Important outdoor pest.

Western tree hole mosquito, *Aedes varipalpus*

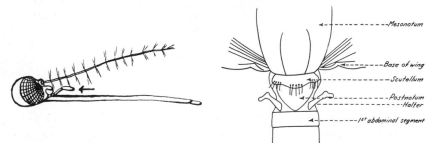

Palps entirely dark; scutellum with narrow yellowish scales. Temporary pools. Southern Canada, eastern United States, west to New Mexico. Important outdoor pest.

*Aedes atropalpus*

789. (787) Hind tarsi with broad white rings basally and apically on all segments except the last, which is entirely white; thorax clothed dorsally with golden brown scales. Temporary to semi-

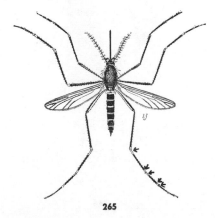

permanent pools. Widespread in forested areas of United States, Canada. Outdoor pest.

*Aedes canadensis canadensis*

Hind tarsi with narrow white rings basally and apically on segments 1 and 2 and basally on segment 3, the remaining segments entirely dark; thorax clothed dorsally with blackish brown scales and a very narrow median longitudinal line of golden brown scales. Temporary pools. Southeastern United States. Minor outdoor pest.

*Aedes canadensis mathesoni*

790. (766) Postspiracular bristles (psp) absent. Tree holes. Southwestern United States. Habits uncertain.

*Aedes purpureipes*

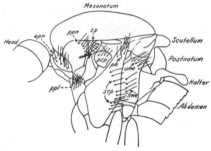

Postspiracular bristles present.                                    791

791. (790) Integument of thorax with a pair of dark brown or black posterolateral spots; pleuron (side) of thorax with a dark brown spot beneath the anterior spiracle; abdominal tergites yellow scaled basally (front margin) and laterally (sides), dark scaled apically (hind margin). Flood pools. Southeastern United States to Oklahoma and Texas. Outdoor pest.

*Aedes fulvus pallens*

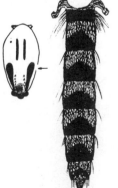

Integument of thorax lacking posterolateral dark brown or black spots.                                    792

792. (791) Thorax with a broad median longitudinal stripe or patch of silver white or pale yellow scales, *or* with sides and anterior margin clothed with silver white scales (illust. 793).    793
Thorax not marked with silver white scales.    795

793. (792) Thorax with a broad median stripe of dark brown scales, the stripe broader posteriorly, sides and anterior margin with silver white scales. Tree holes. Southern Canada, eastern United States into South. Important outdoor pest.
*Aedes triseriatus*

Thorax with a broad median stripe or patch of silver white scales *or* pale yellow scales.    794

794. (793) Median longitudinal stripe of thorax extending from anterior margin to a little beyond middle, much broader than dark scaled area on either side. Temporary pools. Important outdoor pest. Southeastern United States to Texas.
*Aedes infirmatus*
Extreme southern United States, *Aedes scapularis*

Median longitudinal stripe extending the full length of thorax, usually narrower than the dark scaled area on either side; medium sized species, wing length about 3.5 mm.; occiput (back top of head) dorsally with a median stripe of narrow white scales bounded submedially by a patch of broad

dark scales. Temporary pools. Southeastern United States to New York and Kansas. Important outdoor pest.

*Aedes atlanticus;*
southern United States to Mexico, *Aedes tormentor*

795. (792) Thorax with a pair of broad submedian white or yellowish white stripes separated by a brown stripe of about the same width. Temporary pools. Northern United States, southern Canada. Important outdoor pest, potential encephalitis vector.

*Aedes trivittatus*

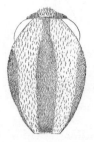

Thorax not marked with 2 broad submedian white or yellowish white stripes.                                                                     796

796. (795) Abdominal tergites with median basal patches of white scales. Temporary pools. Southwestern United States, Florida keys. Habits uncertain.

*Aedes thelcter*

Abdominal tergites with complete or partial basal pale bands, without pale bands *or* almost completely pale scaled.    797

797. (796) Wing scales distinctly bicolored.                              798
Wing scales entirely dark *or* with only white scaled patches at bases of veins *or* with scattered pale scales on anterior veins.                                                                        800

798. (797) Wing with dark and pale scales intermixed, the dark predominating; lower mesepimeral bristles (illust. 801 lme) usually present. Temporary pools. Plains of northern United States. Important outdoor pest.

*Aedes niphadopsis*

Wing with alternating black and white scales; lower mesepimeral bristles lacking.　799

799. (798) Abdomen with a dorsal median longitudinal stripe of pale scales or almost entirely pale scaled; scales on dorsal half of posterior pronotum brown. Temporary pools. Plains of northern United States, Canada. Important outdoor pest.

*Aedes spencerii*

Abdomen lacking a dorsal median longitudinal stripe of pale scales; scales on dorsal half of posterior pronotum white or whitish brown. Spring pools. Northwestern United States, southwestern Canada. Important outdoor pest.

*Aedes idahoensis*

800. (797) Thorax lacking contrasting lines or stripes.　801
Thorax with contrasting lines or stripes.　806

801. (800) Lower mesepimeral bristles (lme) present.　802

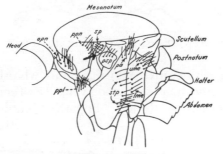

Lower mesepimeral bristles lacking.　805

802. (801) Thorax with many long black or brownish black setae, thus giving a hairy appearance; sternopleuron (illust. 801 stp) with scales extending to anterior angle; scutellum with golden

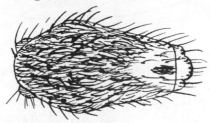

brown scales. Treeless Arctic region of Canada, Alaska to Colorado. Minor outdoor pest.

*Aedes impiger*

Thorax moderately clothed with normal setae.　803

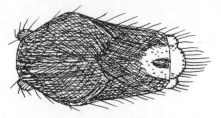

803. (802) Mesepimeron bare on lower 1/4 to 1/3 (illust. 801 lme); occiput and torus with white scales. Ponds and bogs. Northern United States, Canada. Important outdoor pest.

*Aedes intrudens*

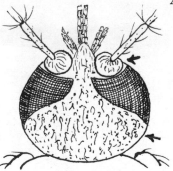

Mesepimeron with scales reaching to lower margin.　804

804. (803) Wing with scattered to numerous whitish scales along costa (c), subcosta (sc), and vein 1. Temporary pools. Northern Rockies northward. Important outdoor pest.

*Aedes cataphylla*

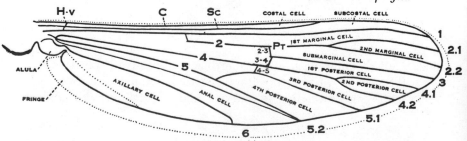

Wing scales dark except for a patch of white scales at base of costa. Important outdoor pest. Spring pools.
Rockies and northward, *Aedes hexodontus;* salt water, Alaska, *Aedes punctodes;* temporary pools, Alaska, northern United States, *Aedes punctor*

805. (801) Coxa of front leg with a central patch of brown scales on anterior margin; occiput (top of head) dorsally with a median patch of broad dark appressed scales. Spring pools. Widespread. Outdoor pest.

*Aedes cinereus*

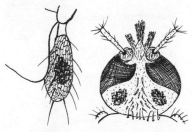

Coxa of front leg clothed with white scales on anterior surface; occiput lacking a submedian patch of broad dark appressed scales on dorsal surface. Snow pools. Mountains of western United States. Important outdoor pest.

*Aedes ventrovittis*

806. (800) Lower mesepimeral bristles (lme) present.          807

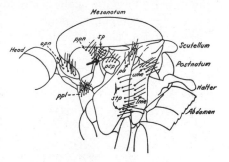

Lower mesepimeral bristles lacking.          814

807. (806) Hypostigial (beneath metathoracic spiracle) spot (illust. 806 ⌇ ) of few to many white scales present.          808
  Hypostigial spot of scales lacking.          811

808.  (807) Proboscis with scattered pale scales to near tip. Temporary pools. California. Minor outdoor pest.

*Aedes bicristatus*

Proboscis entirely white.                                                809

809.  (808) Thorax with paired submedian (near middle) stripes separated by a pair of narrow stripes of light brown scales with a narrow bare faint line between them. Temporary pools. Mountains of western United States, Canada, Alaska. Important outdoor pest.

*Aedes pullatus*

Thorax with a broad median stripe *or* narrowly divided stripes of brown scales.                                          810

810.  (809) Sternopleuron (stp) with scales extending about half-way to anterior angle. Temporary pools. In or near forests of northern United States, Canada, Alaska. Outdoor pest.

*Aedes implicatus*

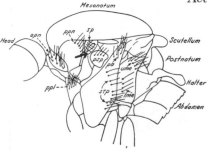

Sternopleuron with scales extending to anterior angle. Spring pools. Forests of northern United States, Canada. Outdoor pest.

*Aedes trichurus*

811. (807) Abdominal tergites with narrow basal pale bands on less than half the segments when present. Spring pools. Forests of northern United States, Canada, Alaska. Outdoor pest.

*Aedes diantaeus*

Abdominal tergites with basal white bands on more than half the segments. 812

812. (811) Proboscis with brown scales on ventral surface; wing usually with a patch of white scales at base of costa. 813

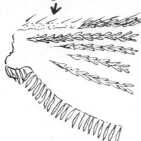

Proboscis as above; wing usually lacking a patch of white scales at base of costa. Temporary cool pools. Outdoor pests. Northwestern United States, Canada, Alaska. Northwest Coast mosquito, *Aedes aboriginis;* northeastern United States, southeastern Canada. Minor pest. *Aedes abserratus;* Alaska, northern United States, *Aedes punctor*

813. (812) Thorax clothed with yellow or yellowish white scales and a pair of rather well defined submedian dark brown stripes *or* with a varying pattern of yellowish white to yellow and dark brown scales; supra-alar bristles (above wing base, ∕ ) generally dark brown to black. Spring pools, temporary to semipermanent. Forests of northern United States, Canada. Important outdoor pests.

*Aedes communis;* Rocky Mountains, Alaska to Colorado.

Habits uncertain, *Aedes pionips*

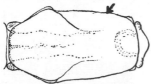

Thorax clothed with yellow scales, occasionally yellowish white to yellowish brown, and a broad median or narrowly divided stripe of dark brown scales; supra-alar bristles generally yellow to dark brown. Spring pools. Rockies and northward. Outdoor pest.

*Aedes hexodontus*

814. (806) Abdomen with basal white bands on more than half the segments; hypostigial spot (✦) of scales lacking; pleuron (side) with median sized patches of pale scales; sternopleuron (stp) with a narrow line of scales reaching near the anterior angle and with scales narrowly separated from the patch of pale scales on the pre-alar (ppn) area. Flood pools. Widespread. United States, Canada. Important outdoor pest.

Floodwater mosquito, *Aedes sticticus*

Abdomen without basal white bands *or* with narrow bands on less than half of the segments.     815

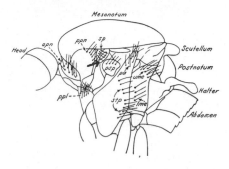

815. (814) Thorax with a broad median, dark stripe, much broader posteriorly (illust. 816).     816

Thorax with 2 narrow brown stripes separated by a narrow line of pale yellow scales, brown stripes sometimes fused, thus forming 1 broad brown stripe but not distinctly broader posteriorly (illust. 817).     817

816. (815) Sternites (underside) of abdomen clothed with grayish white scales; thorax with median dark stripe gradually

 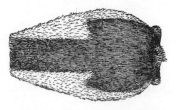

broadened posteriorly. Temporary pools. Northern United States, Canada, east of Rockies. Important outdoor pest.

*Aedes aurifer*

Sternites of abdomen with some of the segments brown scaled apically (near tip); thorax with median dark stripe abruptly broadened posteriorly. Tree holes. Southeastern United States to Ohio and Texas. Important outdoor pest.

*Aedes thibaulti*

817. (815) Occiput (behind eyes) clothed dorsally with narrow curved pale yellow scales; sternopleuron (illust. 814 stp) with about 12-20 setae. Spring pools. Forests of northern United States, Canada, Alaska. Outdoor pest.

*Aedes diantaeus*

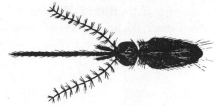

Occiput dorsally with narrow curved pale yellow scales on median area and with subdorsal patches of dark brown appressed scales; sternopleuron usually with 5-6, not more than 10, setae. Temporary pools. Northern United States, Canada, Alaska. Very feeble bite, minor outdoor pest.

*Aedes decticus*

818. (749) Wing scales narrow on vein 2 (see illust. 804); occiput (head behind eyes) usually lacking broad appressed scales dorsally.                                                      819

Wing scales slightly or distinctly broadened on vein 2; occiput usually with broad appressed scales dorsally, sometimes limited to a narrow border behind the eyes; hind tarsal segments entirely dark. Margins of lakes, ponds, streams. Southern United States to Michigan and North Dakota. Minor outdoor pests.

*Culex erraticus* et al.

819. (818) Tarsal segments with rather distinct white rings, the rings on hind legs rather broad; proboscis with a contrasting white ring near middle; femora and tibia each with a longitudinal line of white scales *or* a row of white spots on outer surface; a V-shaped dark marking on sternite of each abdominal segment. Temporary pools. Western, southern, and central United States, southwestern Canada. Structural pest, vector of encephalitis, etc.

*Culex tarsalis*

Tarsal segments without distinct white rings, if rings are pale they are narrow and brownish; abdominal segments with pale scales basal when present.                                    820

820. (819) Thorax bright reddish brown, clothed with narrow hair-like golden brown scales; pleura (side) and coxae (first leg segment) reddish brown. Shallow pools, Southwestern United States to Idaho, Utah and California. Important outdoor pest.

*Culex erythrothorax*

Thorax light brown, brown or dark brown, never reddish brown, clothed with narrow curved scales; pleura and coxae never bright reddish brown.                                    821

821. (820) Abdominal segments each with a rather broad basal band of whitish scales dorsally.                    822

Abdominal segments lacking broad basal whitish band dorsally, pale scaling if present in narrow bands or restricted to lateral patches.                    823

822. (821) Abdominal bands broadly rounded on posterior margin and constricted laterally, rather narrowly joining or entirely disconnected from the lateral patches; scales of thorax somewhat coarse, golden. Develop in water about buildings, artificial containers. Structural pests. United States except extreme South, Canada.

Northern house mosquito, *Culex pipiens*
Southern United States.
Southern house mosquito, *Culex quinquefasciatus*

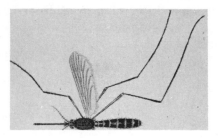

Abdominal bands with posterior margin nearly straight and broadly joining the lateral patches, especially on segments 3-5; scales of thorax fine, golden brown; medium sized, wing length 4-4.4 mm.; thorax usually with a pair of pale scaled submedian spots near middle. Temporary pools. Widespread. Outdoor pest.

*Culex restuans*

823. (821) Pleuron (side) with few or no scales, when present rarely more than 5-6 in a single group. Permanent ponds. Southern United States. Structural pest.

*Culex nigripalpus*

Pleuron with several groups of broad pale scales, each group usually comprised of more than 6 scales; abdominal segments usually with narrow dingy yellow basal bands dorsally and with apices of segments more or less blended with yellowish scales, segment VII either primarily or entirely clothed with dingy yellow scales. Temporary pools. Eastern United States, southeastern Canada to Utah. Structural pest.

*Culex salinarius*

## IMMATURE INSECTS

830. (3) Inactive stages incapable of locomotion (crawling), but may move abdomen, or exhibit feeble wriggling motions. Insect eggs (a), egg capsules (b), and pupae of beetles, moths (c), ants, bees, wasps, fleas, and most flies (d). 839

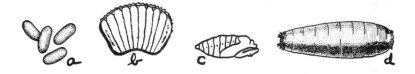

Active stages capable of locomotion (crawling or swimming), or if incapable of locomotion when free, normally enclosed in food media as wood, cereals, and other food products, or in cells or capsules constructed by adults. Larvae and pupae of mosquitoes, fly larvae and maggots, moth caterpillars and beetle, flea, ant, wasp and bee larvae (illust. 832+). 831

831. (830) Thoracic legs well developed, segmented and conspicuous (illust. 832).

Orders COLEOPTERA, LEPIDOPTERA 832

Thoracic legs segmented, but very inconspicuous; *or* represented by fleshy lobes or protuberances (prolegs); *or* absent.

Orders DIPTERA, SIPHONAPTERA,
HYMENOPTERA, few COLEOPTERA     833

832. (831) Three pairs of thoracic legs, and 2 or more pairs of usually well developed prolegs on abdomen, at least some of the latter bearing hooks (crochets, c.); head distinct; body with setae only, never with ovate scales.

Caterpillars, LEPIDOPTERA     860

Thoracic legs as above, typically 3 pairs; not more than 1 pair of prolegs on abdomen, except a very few wood boring Cerambycidae.

Order COLEOPTERA     886

833. (831) Thoracic legs absent, not replaced by prolegs, fleshy lobes, or protuberances.

Orders DIPTERA, SIPHONAPTERA,
HYMENOPTERA, few COLEOPTERA     834

Thoracic legs present, but inconspicuous, or replaced by fleshy lobes or protuberances (prolegs). (illust. 836).

Few COLEOPTERA     838

834. (833) Much enlarged at head end (pupae), the head and thorax with respective appendages being fused; the abdomen tail-like and ending in 2 or 4 broad, flat paddle-like plates, *or* 2 long triangular processes; 2 horns (breathing tubes) projecting from dorsal surface of enlarged head end; aquatic, swim by repeated folding and extension of tail-like abdomen.

Order DIPTERA:
CULICIDAE, MOSQUITO PUPAE     975

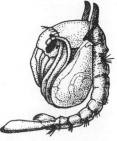

Larvae of various types, not as above.     835

835. (834) Small, length 10 mm. or less; cylindrical; whitish; several long hairs on each segment; head distinct, sclerotized (hard), pigmented, and directed forward; chewing mouthparts; abdomen 10 segmented, the last segment small, with a row of short setae or hairs above on hind margin; spiracles absent or inconspicuous. Scavengers on floors, in crevices, nests, and bedding of hosts.

Order SIPHONAPTERA: FLEAS

Not as above. 836

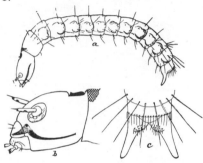

836. (835) Legless and helpless when free; in nests constructed by adults in soil, attached to structures, trees and other objects, or in cavities, crevices, and hollows enclosed by adults; nests often constructed of paper, wax, or mud or enclosed in cavities with similar materials; frequently attended by adults; food stored for larvae or brought to them daily by adults; larvae are not structural pests directly.

Order HYMENOPTERA: BEES, WASPS, ANTS 947

Not as above. 837

837. (836) Infest wood and wood products and/or dry cereal foods, sometimes dried fruits.

Order COLEOPTERA:
some CERAMBYCIDAE, BRUCHIDAE
SCOLYTIDAE, all BUPRESTIDAE
and ANTHRIBIDAE 886

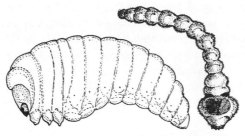

Not in above products unless unusually wet; usually in water or moist media, a few (Scenopinidae) in dry situations.

Order DIPTERA    952

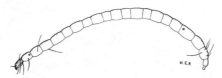

838. (833) Thoracic legs present, but inconspicuous, hidden, or poorly developed.

Order COLEOPTERA:
some ANOBIIDAE, BOSTRICHIDAE,
most CERAMBYCIDAE, all LYCTIDAE
and MURMIDIIDAE    886

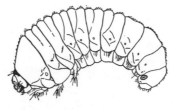

Thoracic legs absent, but replaced by prolegs in the form of unsegmented lobes or protuberances.

Order COLEOPTERA:
Some SCOLYTIDAE and CERAMBYCIDAE,
all CURCULIONIDAE    886

839. (830) No evidence of wings, legs, antennae or mouthparts externally (illust. 841).    840

Projections extending from surface: wings, legs, antennae and mouthparts external and noticeable, *or* if internal, outlines of these appendages visible; often covered or enclosed in cocoons of silk (illust. 854, 855).

PUPAE    853

840. (839) An elongated packet or capsule, at least partially ringed or segmented, rounded or flattened, without appendages; light to dark reddish brown to almost black (illust. 841).    841

Various sizes and shapes, minute to small; often beautifully designed with sculpturing and lines, but never appearing as partially ringed or segmented (illust. 851, 852).

Various INSECT EGGS    851

841. (840) Capsules flattened; a definite ridge or seam (keel) along 1 edge.

Order ORTHOPTERA: family BLATTIDAE:

ROACHES    842

Capsules cylindrical, ends rounded, lacking seam; central longitudinal line extending for few segments at smaller end; opposite end roughened.

Order DIPTERA: FLY PUPARIA

842. (841) Egg chambers fully outlined across walls of capsule on both sides.    843

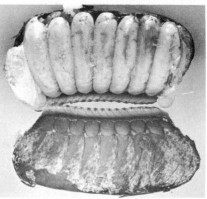

Egg chamber outlines readily visible near seam or    keel edge of capsule only.    847

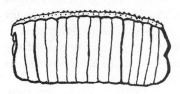 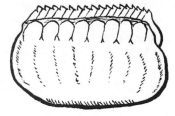

843. (842) Capsule white or pale yellow, very thin; about 20 egg
chambers per side; very large, about 25 mm. long; hatch before or as soon as dropped.

Madeira roach, *Leucophaea maderae*

Capsule tan to dark reddish brown; much smaller, less than
20 mm. long.                                                          844

844. (843) Capsule somewhat rounded or kidney-shaped, not flattened; color brown to dark brown; usually 6 mm. or less in
length (illust. 845).                                                 845

Capsule flattened, color tan to light brown; usually more
than 5 mm. long (illust. 846).                                        846

845. (844) Capsule very small, about 2-4 mm. long; kidney-
shaped, not flattened, curved on both edges; about 9 chambers
per side; color brown to dark brown.

Spotted Mediterranean roach, *Ectobius pallidus*

Capsule about 4-6 mm. long, back side much shorter than
keel side, thus ends are sharply angled away from keel; about
8 egg chambers per side (illust. 850g also); yellowish to reddish brown.

Brown-banded roach, *Supella supellectilium*

846. (844) Capsules indoors, much flattened, twice as long as wide, about 10-12 mm. long (illust. 850f also); usually 18-24 egg chambers per side; 1 end light colored and pliable, shading to darker brown and more firm at free end.

German roach, *Blattella germanica*

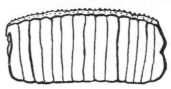

Capsule usually outdoors, 5-8 mm. long, longer than wide; up to 28-32 egg chambers per side; horny in composition; color brown to deep brown.

Woodroaches, *Parcoblatta* spp.

847. (842) Capsules with about 8 egg chambers per side.                 848
      Capsules with about 12-14 egg chambers per side.                 849

848. (847) Capsule length usually less than twice the width, about 8-10 mm. long (illust. 850b also).

American roach, *Periplaneta americana*

Capsule length about twice the width, about 10-12 mm. long (illust. 850d also).

Oriental roach, *Blatta orientalis*

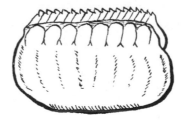

849. (847) Capsule with about 13, sometimes less, egg chambers per side; long and slender; variable; about 12-14 mm. long (illust. 850a also).

Smoky brown roach, *Periplaneta fuliginosa*

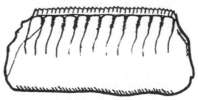

Capsule with about 14, sometimes less, egg chambers per side.                 850

850. (849) Capsule about 10-12 mm. long (variable) (illust. 850c).
Brown roach, *Periplaneta brunnea*

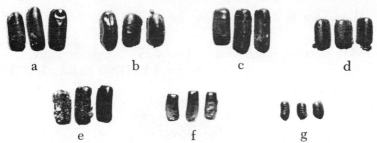

a        b        c        d

e        f        g

Capsule about 9-12 mm. long (variable) (illust. 850e).
Australian roach, *Periplaneta australasiae*

851. (840) Elongated and smooth; pale or white; single or in loose masses; deposited on moist media and surfaces. Common flies: house, stable, blow, etc.

FLIES

Of various shapes or in attached masses; not as above.     852

852. (851) Attached in rafts (masses) that float on water (A); *or* single with lateral extensions that keep them afloat (C); or eggs single, deposited on dry or moist soil, seldom observed (B).

Mosquitoes: *Culex, Anopheles*, et al.
Various INSECT EGGS

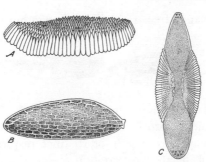

Not as above.

853. (839) Pupae, or larvae, enclosed in cocoons of silk (illust. 854, 855).                                                                            854

Pupae not in or covered by cocoons of silk.                    856

854. (853) Cocoons much longer than wide, 5 mm. or more.
Order LEPIDOPTERA: MOTHS

Cocoons round, less than 4 mm. in greatest dimension.          855

855. (854) Cocoons round, usually embedded in food of larvae.
Order COLEOPTERA:
family PTINIDAE, SPIDER BEETLES

Cocoons round in outline, flattened dorso-ventrally; hidden in cracks, crevices and debris, often attached to fabric or debris.
Order SIPHONAPTERA: FLEAS

856. (853) All appendages fused with each other and to body wall on the side and under surface of thorax.                            857

All appendages free, rarely fused together or to body wall at any point.                                                              858

857. (856) One pair of wings showing in outline; head and thorax usually combined into 1 large area; forms living in wet environments may have a pair of distinct respiratory organs on upper side of head-thorax region.
Order DIPTERA: FLIES

Two pairs of prominent wings closely wrapped about the side and under surfaces, the inner pair largely concealed by the outer pair; antennae adjacent to margins of wings; lacking special respiratory developments; often in silk cocoon.

Order LEPIDOPTERA: MOTHS

858. (856) One pair of wings.

Order DIPTERA: FLIES

Two distinct pairs of wings (illust. 859).                    859

859. (858) Front wings largest and with more veins than hind wings; a distinct constriction between thorax and abdomen; mouthparts for chewing and licking, mandibles opposable; resemble adult ants, wasps or bees.

Order HYMENOPTERA:
ANTS, BEES, WASPS

Front wings resemble wing covers of beetles, few veins visible; pronotum prominent, distinct; chewing mouthparts; resemble beetles in appearance.

Order COLEOPTERA:
BEETLES and WEEVILS

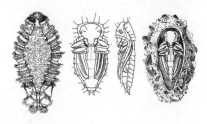

# LEPIDOPTERA (Caterpillars)

860. (832) Prolegs rudimentary, each bearing only 2 or 3 crochets (c) on abdominal prolegs; length up to 7 mm.; inside kernels of grains. Cereal pests. Widespread.

GELECHIIDAE, Angoumois grain moth,
*Sitotroga cerealella*

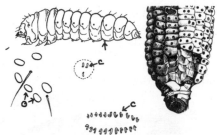

Prolegs more developed, each bearing a number of crochets.     861

861. (860) Four pairs of prolegs; thorax and abdomen with numerous wart-like tubercles clothed with pointed spines and long, slender hairs; body yellowish with 2 brownish dorsal stripes, sometimes lateral lines of same color; length up to 9-14 mm., width 3-4 mm.; head and legs yellow to brown. Introduced into storage with sorghum seed, which was attacked in field. Widespread.

NOLIDAE: sorghum webworm,
*Celama sorghiella*

Five pairs of prolegs.     862

862. (861) Body with primary setae only, lacking tufted or secondary hairs; tubercle VI on abdomen (illust. 865) (near and above proleg) with 1 seta, tubercle VII on proleg with 3 setae; prolegs on sixth abdominal segment; crochets arranged in a complete or incomplete circle (illust. 865, 866), *or* more than 1 length; prespiracular tubercle (pst) of prothorax with 2 setae.     863

As above, except prespiracular tubercle (pst) on prothorax with 3 setae, distinctly separated from pronotal plate (pp).   864

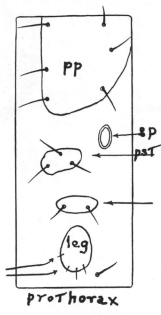

*proThorax*

863. (862) Tubercle VI on mesothorax (near and above leg) with 2 setae.

GALLERIDAE:
*Galleria, Achroia, Aphomia, Corcyra*   867

Tubercle VI on mesothorax with 1 seta.
PYRALIDIDAE: *Pyralis, Hypsopygia;*
PHYCITIDAE: *Plodia, Anagaster, Ephestia*   867

864. (862) Only 2 or 3 crochets (c) on abdominal prolegs; prolegs poorly developed; 6 ocelli (o); white with yellow head, mouthparts dark reddish brown; up to 7 mm. Develop within single kernels.

GELECHIIDAE:
Angoumois grain moth, *Sitotroga cerealella*

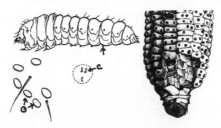

Crochets (c) of prolegs arranged in a complete or partial circle (illust. 866) or ellipse (illust. 865).                    865

865. (864) Setae IV and V (near and generally below spiracle (sp) on abdominal (a) segments far apart (remote), or V lacking; prespiracular setae on prothorax close together, 1 1/2- 2 times as far from spiracle as from each other (illust. 862 pst); abdominal prolegs with crochets (c) arranged in a single complete ellipse.

TINEIDAE:
*Tineola, Tinea, Trichophaga*     869

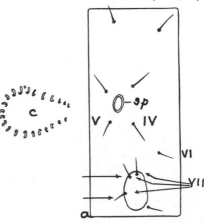

Setae IV and V (near and below spiracle) on abdominal segments close together (adjacent).                    866

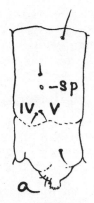

866. (865) Body color wine red, head pale brown, mouthparts blackish, pronotal plate (pp) dark brown; pinnacula (p) lacking or indistinct; 6 ocelli; crochets of sixth abdominal segment with single row of hooks of uneven length in a complete circle; metathoracic legs wide apart, the distance being 1 1/2-2 times the width of the coxae; up to 7-8 mm.

COSMOPTERYGIDAE (LAVERNIDAE): pink corn worm, *Pyroderces rileyi*

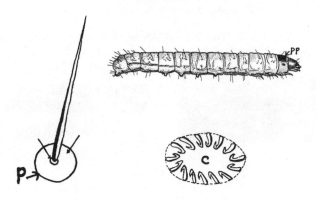

Color not wine red; distance between metathoracic coxae distinctly less than 1 1/2-2 times the width of coxae; ocelli 2-4 on each side.

OECOPHORIDAE: *Hofmannophila, Endrosis* 869

867. (863) Common in beeswax in storage or in hives; occasionally in dried fruits, etc. 868

Infest cereals, tobacco, dried fruits, dry condiments, nuts, chocolate, powdered milk, animal fibers, etc. 869

868. (867) Four ocelli on each side of head, 2 being joined; pale yellowish to grayish brown; pale yellowish spiracles; stout; up to 23-28 mm. long, 4-5 mm. wide.

Greater wax moth, *Galleria mellonella*

Ocelli lacking; white to pale grayish white; black spiracles; slender; up to 15-18 mm. long, 2.5-3 mm. wide.

Lesser wax moth, *Achroia grisella*

869. (865, 866, 867) Common on finished and unfinished animal fibers as wool, fur, and feathers; occasionally in plant materials as cereals, yeast, etc.    870

Feeding primarily on plant materials as cereals, dry condiments, tobacco, dried fruits, nuts, chocolate, powdered milk, etc.    874

870. (869) Larvae live in portable cigar-shaped or broadly swollen cases open at 1 or both ends, composed of silk and food (fabric) fibers, which they drag about (illust. 871).    871

Larvae spin silk webs and tubes, but not cases (illust. 873).    872

871. (870) Cases slender, slightly larger in center than at ends, open at 1 end; larvae with 1 distinct ocellus; up to 10 mm. long.

Casemaking clothes moth, *Tinea pellionella*

Cases broad, much wider in central portion, open at both ends; larvae lacking ocelli.

Plaster bagworm, *Tineola walsinghami*

872. (870) Four ocelli on each side of head; trochanters of front legs lacking a swelling (gibbosity) on inner or ventral side; white, head reddish brown, tips of jaws black; up to 18 mm. long, 3 mm. wide. Attack fabrics and cereals.

Brown house moth,
*Hofmannophila pseudospretella*

Less than 4 ocelli.    873

873. (872) Ocelli lacking; spiracles of seventh and eighth abdominal segments about equal in size; white, shiny and greasy appearing; often in loose tunnel-like silk tubes attached to fabric; up to 13 mm. long.

Webbing clothes moth, *Tineola bisselliella*

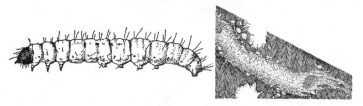

One distinct ocellus; spiracles of seventh abdominal segment 1/2 to 2/3 the size of eighth abdominal spiracle; whitish, head black, thoracic shield dark; burrow in thick fabrics; spin loose webs or tubes; up to 13 mm. long.

Carpet moth, *Trichophaga tapetzella*

874. (869) Largely attacking whole grains as corn and wheat; small emergence holes noticeable on each kernel.    875
Largely attacking broken grains, meals or flours, and other plant foods.    876

875. (874) Prolegs rudimentary or lacking, each bearing 2-3 crochets; develop within a single kernel; white with yellow head, mouthparts dark reddish brown; up to 7 mm.

Angoumois grain moth, *Sitotroga cerealella*

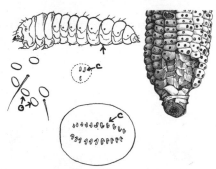

Prolegs well developed; larvae pass from 1 kernel to another, webbing them together; yellowish white with reddish brown head, 2 curved brown stripes on body; 6 ocelli on each side; spiracle of seventh abdominal segment about 3/4 the size of spiracle of eighth segments.

European grain moth,
*Nemapogon (Tinea) granella*

876. (874) Largely lacking pinnacula (dark or pale sclerotized areas about hairs or setae, (p) over most of body; attack many plant products.　　　　　　　　　　　　　　　　877

Bearing pinnacula over most of body; attack many plant food products.　　　　　　　　　　　　　　　　879

877. (876) Dirty white, decidedly grayish on thorax, first and hind abdominal segments, with intermediate abdominal segments paler; spiracles dark, conspicuous; 4 ocelli on each side, 2 being fused; up to 20-25 mm. long, 3-4 mm. wide.

Meal moth, *Pyralis farinalis*

Not as above; up to 15 mm. long.　　　　　　　　　878

878. (877) Cuticle dull white, distinct pinnacula (illust. 876) lacking on first 7 abdominal segments; spiracular rim about twice as thick on hind margin as front margin; up to 15 mm. long, 3 mm. wide.

Rice moth, *Corcyra cephalonica*

Grayish or dirty white, head, mouthparts, claws, and crochets pale yellowish brown to reddish brown; pinnacula lacking on meso and metathorax and first 9 abdominal segments; spiracle less conspicuous and rim of about equal thickness before and behind; 6, or 5, ocelli on each side; crochets of first 4 prolegs in complete circles; up to 10-13 mm. long, 1.8-2.2 mm. wide.

Indian meal moth, *Plodia interpunctella*

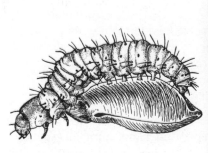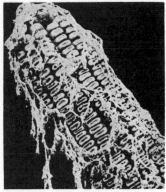

879. (876) Two ocelli on each side; spiracle of eighth abdominal segment round or nearly so; trochanter of front leg with large prominent swelling on inner surface; white; up to 10-11 mm. long, 1.5-2 mm. wide.

*Endrosis sarcitrella*

Six, sometimes 5, ocelli on each side.      880

880. (879) Dark colored larvae, pale brown to black, often with dark patches; head pale reddish brown; pronotal plate, legs, crochets, and setae yellowish to reddish brown; spiracles dark brown to black; 15-17 mm. long, 2-3 mm. wide.

*Hypsopygia costalis*

Larvae light colored, white, grayish white to pinkish or greenish; head, mouthparts, parts of legs, and crochets and spiracles pale to dark yellowish brown; pinnacula conspicuous, yellow to brown.      881

881. (880) Six ocelli on each side; whitish to grayish white; head, including mouthparts, and pronotal plate dark reddish brown; crochets of prolegs pale reddish brown, forming a complete circle on first 4 prolegs; peritremes of spiracles (sp) black, roundish; pinnacula (p) of thorax and abdomen smoky brown;

sp

p

spiracle rims about equal in thickness on all sides; up to 25-30 mm. long, 3-4 mm. wide.

*Aphomia gularis*

Six, sometimes 5, ocelli on each side; white to pinkish or greenish; pinnacula conspicuous, yellow to brown; dorsal rim of spiracle narrow in comparison to broad sides; large sclerotized ring enclosing a membranous area at base of seta III of mesothorax and abdominal segment 8 (illust. 883, 884).          882

882. (881) Brown or purple spots in rows on back; seta IIIa of eighth abdominal segment separated from spiracle (sp) by a distance about equal to or distinctly less than diameter of spiracle (illust. 883).

*Ephestia cautella, E. figulilella*     883

Lacking brown or purple spots on back; seta IIIa separated from spiracle (sp) by a distance 2-3 times the diameter of spiracle (illust. 884).

*Ephestia elutella, Anagasta (Ephestia)*
*kuhniella (sericarium)*     884

883. (882) Common in dried figs, dates, raisins and nuts; also many cereal products, etc.; seta IIIa of eighth abdominal segment separated from spiracle (sp) by a distance distinctly less than diameter of spiracle; up to 12-14 mm. long, 1.8-2 mm. wide.

Almond moth, *Ephestia cautella*

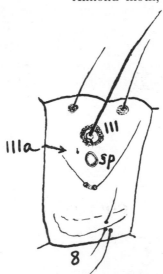

Common on dried fruits and nuts; also many cereal products, etc.; seta IIIa separated from spiracle (sp) by a distance approximately equal to diameter of spiracles; up to 10-12 mm. long, 1.3 mm. wide.

Raisin moth, *Ephestia figulilella*

884. (882) Common in tobacco, chocolate, and many cereal products; spiracle of eighth abdominal segment not more than 2/3 as broad as membranous area enclosed by sclerotized ring around base of seta III; up to 10-15 mm. long, 1-1.5 mm. wide.

Tobacco moth, *Ephestia elutella*

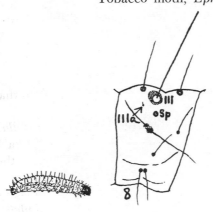

Very common in many cereal products, dried fruits, nuts, etc.; produce extensive webbing; spiracle (sp) of eighth abdominal segment about the diameter of membranous area enclosed by sclerotized ring around base of seta III; up to 15-20 mm., 2-3 mm. wide.

Mediterranean flour moth,
*Anagasta* (*Ephestia*) *kuhniella*

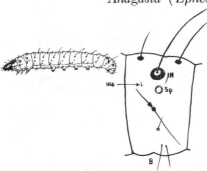

## COLEOPTERA

886. (832, 837, 838) C-shaped, crescent-shaped, or humpbacked.    887

Not as above, usually elongate.    903

887. (886) Thorax lacking segmented legs, which are replaced by fleshy lobes (illust. 889). 888

Thorax with segmented legs, but usually reduced, inconspicuous, or hidden (illust. 895). 893

888. (887) Feed inside seeds, whole grains, coffee, dried fruit, macaroni, sphaghetti; common. 889

In wood. 890

889. (888) Body about the same thickness throughout its length; hairy. Southern.

PLATYSTOMIDAE: coffee bean weevil,
*Araecerus fasciculatus*

Body short and stubby, much thicker in middle; relatively smooth. Widespread.

CURCULIONIDAE:
granary and rice weevils, *Sitophilus* spp. 477

890. (888) Feeding between inner bark and phloem (solid wood), leave characteristic engraving on wood. Often in firewood; do not attack dry wood.

SCOLYTIDAE: ENGRAVER BEETLES

Feeding in solid wood. 891

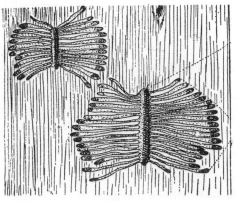

891. (890) Dark stains in wood surrounding burrows. Often in flooring and firewood. Do not attack dry wood.

SCOLYTIDAE: AMBROSIA BEETLES

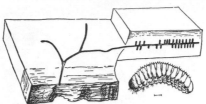

Stains lacking; attack soft wood lumber and furniture (illust. 892).

CURCULIONIDAE: WOOD WEEVILS    892

892. (891) Frass very fine and powdery.

*Hexarthrum* spp., *Cossonus* spp.

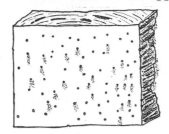

Frass coarser, not a fine powder.

*Pissodes* spp. et al.

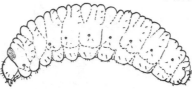

893. (887) Develop in legumes; beans and peas; 3-5 mm. long. (Most readily identified as adults.)

BRUCHIDAE    894

Develop in wood or cereal products.    896

894. (893) Infest peas in field only, but may emerge in storage; one generation annually.

Pea weevil, *Bruchus pisorum*

Infest beans and peas in the field and in storage; repeated generations; 4.5-5 mm.

895

895. (894) Cowpeas the favorite food, but infest other peas and beans; 3.5-4 mm.

Southern cowpea weevil, *Callosobruchus maculatus*

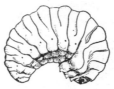

Beans the favorite food, but infest a wide variety of beans and peas; 4-4.5 mm.

Bean weevil, *Acanthoscelides obtectus*

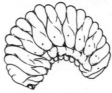

896. (893) Three pairs of inconspicuous thoracic legs, 3 segmented, terminating in a long claw; spiracle of eighth (last) abdominal segment conspicuous, elliptical, and 3 times the size of earlier abdominal spiracles; creamy white; 3-5 mm. Develop in wood. (For further identification see adults.)

LYCTIDAE

Not as above.                                                                                      897

897. (896) Three pairs of well-developed thoracic legs, with 4-5 segments, terminating in a single claw; abdominal spiracles about equal in size; dirty white; 3-5 mm. Usually develop in plant food products.

PTINIDAE

Not as above.                                                                                      898

898. (897) Thoracic segments broader than rest of body; legs, 4 segmented, hairy, sometimes reduced; white; 3 mm. or more in length. Attack wood and cereal products (illust. 899).

BOSTRICHIDAE    899

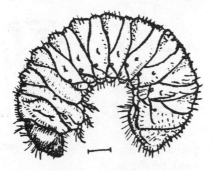

Thoracic segments about the size, sometimes broader than abdominal segments; legs well-developed, 4 segmented, not hairy, sometimes reduced; white; 3-10 mm. Attack wood and cereal products (illust. 902).

ANOBIIDAE    901

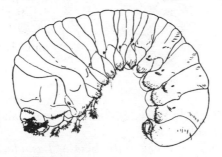

899. (898) In grain and cereal products.                                   900
    In wood. (For further identification see adults.)
                                           BOSTRICHIDAE

900. (899) Well-developed larvae about 3.2 mm. long; widespread.
                    Lesser grain borer, *Rhyzopertha dominica*

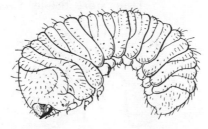

Well-developed larvae about 4.2 mm. long. Southern, uncommon.

Larger grain borer, *Prostephanus truncatus*

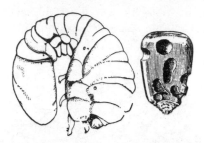

901. (898) In grain, cereal products, tobacco, etc.      902
In wood, or wood products.

ANOBIIDAE

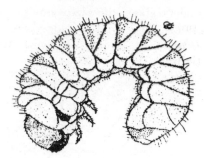

902. (901) Conspicuously hairy; 2-3 mm. Tobacco and cereal products. Widespread.

Cigarette beetle, *Lasioderma serricorne*

Not conspicuously hairy, but has numerous short hairs; 2-3 mm. Wide variety of plant materials. Widespread.

Drug store beetle, *Sitodrepa panicea*

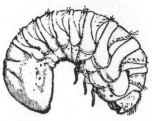

903. (886) Wood feeders.                                              904
       Feed on stored foods and other products, but not on wood,
   although occasionally penetrating wood for pupation.               908

904. (903) Develop in moist to wet wood in contact with water
   or soil as wharf piling, foundations, etc.; thorax and first 4
   abdominal segments wider than remaining abdominal segments;
   thoracic legs well-developed, 4 segmented; up to about 30 mm.
                                OEDEMERIDAE: wharf borer,
                                        *Nacerda melanura*

       Not in wet wood; legs absent, or not well-developed, 5 seg-
   mented.                                                            905

905. (904) Legless; prothorax much enlarged and wider than other
   segments; head small and retracted in prothorax; abdomen
   long, slender, flattened from above; up to 50 mm. or more.
   Bore and feed in solid wood, often in firewood.
                                        BUPRESTIDAE:
                        FLAT-HEADED BORERS, WOOD BORERS

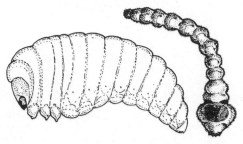

       Legs absent, reduced to mere spines, or up to inconspicuous
   5 segmented legs; thorax a little wider than abdomen; head
   well-defined, retracted in prothorax; abdomen constricted between segments; up to 80 mm. or more in length. Bore in
   wood, often in firewood, sometimes in lumber.
               CERAMBYCIDAE: ROUND-HEADED BORERS,
                  LONG-HORNED BORERS, WOOD BORERS      906

906. (905) Legs absent.
                          Sawyer beetles, *Monochamus* spp.
       Legs reduced or inconspicuous.                                 907

907. (906) In dry wood in buildings, capable of continuous rein-
festation; 3 ocelli on each side of head; prothorax with deep
longitudinal groove; legs short, inconspicuous, 4 segmented.
Old house borer or house bock,
*Hylotrupes bajulus*

Not as above.

Other CERAMBYCIDAE    908

908. (903, 907) Urogomphi (paired processes projecting from up-
perside of ninth or last large abdominal segment) absent or
rudimentary.    909

Urogomphi present.    930

909. (908) Resembling sowbugs, much flattened, about twice as
long as wide; head and appendages concealed beneath body;
setae outlining entire margin of body; pronotum longer than
meso and metathorax combined; 1-1.5 mm.
MURMIDIIDAE: *Murmidius ovalis*

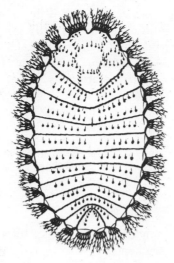

Not as above, more elongate.                                910

910. (909) Dark colored, brown to black; hairy or with tufts of
     hairs.
                                DERMESTIDAE      911
        Light colored, white to light brown; relatively smooth.   929

911. (910) Long and narrow, tapering toward hind end; body cov-
     ered with golden brown to very dark brown hairs lying flat
     on body, giving it a silk-like sheen; hind end with a long tuft
     of brown hairs nearly as long as body; dorsal surface lacks seg-
     mented tufts of spear-headed hairs; up to 7-8 mm. (illust. 912).
                        BLACK CARPET BEETLES     912
        Not as above.                                             913

912. (911) Golden yellow in coloration, *or* chestnut brown in colora-
     tion. (Become darker just preceding molting.)  Two varieties
     or species of

                Black carpet beetle, *Attagenus piceus*
                Other species of *Attagenus*

     Not as above.

913. (911) Larvae stout, brownish, with a dense covering of short bristles, a single transverse row of stiff erect hairs on each segment; lack spear-headed, segmented hairs above; curls into a ball when disturbed; length up to 5-6 mm. Female resembles larvae. Feeds on animal matter as dead insects, museum specimens, etc.

Odd beetle, *Thylodrias contractus*

Spear-headed, segmented hairs above; tufts of spear-headed hairs on last few segments.                                914

914. (913) V-shaped tufts of spear-headed hairs (slender hairs with sharply pointed overlapping scales) arising from an entirely membranous area, usually converging over the cauda, on sides of abdominal segments V, VI, and VII, tufts absent on segment VIII (illust. 916).

Carpet beetles, *Anthrenus* spp.   915

Tufts of spear-headed hairs arising from distinctly sclerotized (hard and pigmented) areas, not obviously converging over cauda; tufts on segment VIII.

Cabinet beetles, *Trogoderma* spp.   918

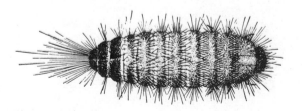

915. (914) Abdomen membranous beneath; antennae with second segment less than 2 1/2 times as long as broad.    916

Abdomen sclerotized (hard and pigmented) beneath, antennae with second segment 5 times as long as broad.    917

916. (915) Heads of spear-headed hairs of hind tufts as long as combined length of 4-5 preceding segments.

*Anthrenus museorum*

Heads of spear-headed hairs of hind tufts about 0.04 mm. long, equal to combined length of 7-8 preceding segments; up to 4-5 mm.

Varied carpet beetle, *Anthrenus verbasci*

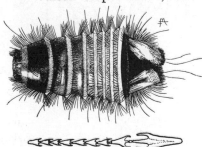

917. (915) Heads of spear-headed hairs of hind tufts about 0.17 mm. long; length up to 4-5 mm.

Common carpet beetle,
*Anthrenus scrophulariae*

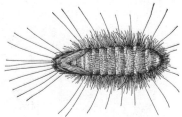

Heads of spear-headed hairs of hind tufts about 0.10 mm. long, equal to 14 of preceding segments; length up to 5 mm.

Furniture carpet beetle,
*Anthrenus flavipes (vorax)*

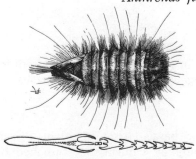

918. (914) Each body segment above, (tergite, t) bearing numerous short, blunt, inwardly directed spear-headed setae, which are about twice as thick as pointed setae of acrotergite, a; setae of basal (first) segment of antennae (difficult to see) less than half as long as second segment; second segment 3 times as long as first. Largely western.

*Trogoderma simplex*

    Tergites lacking numerous short, blunt, inwardly directed setae; setae of basal segment of antennae at least 3/4 as long as second segment.    919

919. (918) Body color generally dark, coxae grayish brown over most of ventral (under) surface; setae of basal segment of antennae encircling segment, some extending beyond tip of second segment. Northern states and Canada.

*Trogoderma sinistrum*

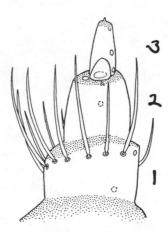

    Usually light in color, coxae cream colored or hyaline (transparent), or largely so, over ventral surface.    920

920. (919) Setae of basal (first) segment of antennae almost completely encircling segment, not bunched on one side, ex-

tending to tip of second segment or beyond when antenna is extended. 921

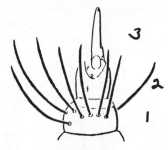

Setae of basal segment of antennae bunched on one side of segment, not reaching tip of second segment when antennae is extended; 1/3 or more of outer part of segment bare. 924

921. (920) Antecostal suture (transverse line or groove near front margin of segment) distinct across seventh and eighth abdominal segments, or eighth rarely interrupted at midline. (Hairs should be removed to increase visibility.) 922

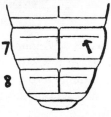

Antecostal suture on first 7 abdominal segments, lacking or interrupted, if present, on eighth segment. 923

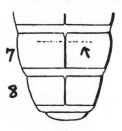

922. (921) Creamy yellow to light brown above, lacking areas of darker gray; head (h) of spear-headed hairs 0.6 mm. long, equal to about 4 of preceding segments. Widespread.

*Trogoderma inclusum*

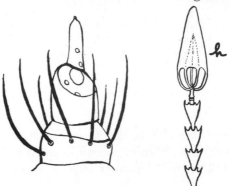

Thorax and usually first 5-6 abdominal segments dark gray, or in teneral (new) forms creamy yellow with grayish spots. Northern United States.

*Trogoderma glabrum*

923. (921) Uniformly creamy yellow to medium brown above; setae of basal (first) antennal segment reach beyond the tip of second segment when antenna is extended. Southwest and Mexico.

Khapra beetle, *Trogoderma granarium*

Thorax and usually first 5-6 abdominal segments above light brown in middle and grayish brown on sides, dark grayish brown occasionally extending across segments; setae of first segment of antennae just reaching the tip of second segment. Widespread in Midwest.

*Trogoderma teukton*

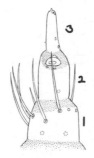

924. (920) Setae of acrotergites (front portion of segment) all or nearly all long enough to extend across antecostal suture; sensory pores of third antennal segment are at or beyond basal fourth of segment; papillae of second segment pointed distally.    925

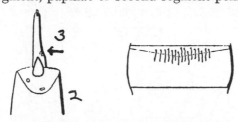

Anterior setae of acrotergites not extending across antecostal suture, at least one sensory pore of third segment of antennae in basal portion of segment.    928

925. (924) Fully pigmented specimens darker on front half of second and third thoracic segments than on first segment (pronotum); one or 2 setae usually present on second antennal segment. Widespread.

*Trogoderma sternale*

Fully pigmented specimens with thorax uniform in color, light or dark; setae present or lacking on second antennal segment.    926

926. (925) Back half of middle thoracic segment (mesonotum) above with numerous spear-headed setae, always smaller than the largest spear-headed setae across the middle of segment; one or 2 setae usually present on second segment of antenna; color creamy yellow, never dark. Western.

*Trogoderma sternale plagifer*

Back half of middle thoracic segment above with few spear-headed setae as stout as those across the middle of segment, these latter numerous; second segment of antennae lacking setae.    927

927. (926) Creamy yellow above; antecostal sutures of seventh and eighth abdominal segments not extending completely across segments, may be lacking on eighth; basal sensory pores of terminal antennal segment situated beyond the basal third;

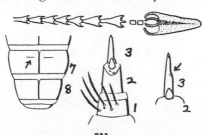

head of spear-headed hairs .03 mm. long, equal to 3-4 of preceding segments (illust. 928 lower). Widespread.

Cabinet beetle, *Trogoderma ornatum*

Yellowish brown to medium brown above; antecostal sutures of seventh and eighth abdominal segments complete; sensory pores of third antennal segment at about the basal fourth. Southwest and West.

*Trogoderma grassmani*

928. (924) Setae sparse on disc (center) of thoracic and front abdominal segments above, those at base (front) of first abdominal segment short, at least some not reaching beyond antecostal suture; large erect setae of median row in single series; antecostal suture of eighth abdominal segment complete (illust. 927 lower), except an occasional interruption at middle. Northern and Southwest United States.

*Trogoderma parabile*

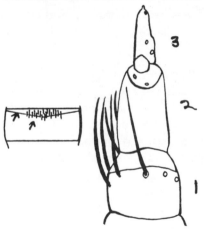

Setae dense across disc of thoracic and anterior abdominal segments, those of median row in double rank; antecostal sutures of seventh and eighth abdominal segments not complete, suture on eighth may be lacking (illust. 927 upper). Widespread.

Cabinet beetle, *Trogoderma ornatum*

929. (910) Antennae with 3 segments, the second 2-4 times the length of the first, the third nearly as long as second; spiracles circular and inconspicuous; length up to 2 mm.

LATHRIDIIDAE:
fungus beetle, *Cartoderes* et al.

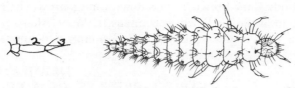

Antennae with 3 segments, the second the longest, the third very small; spiracles circular and conspicuous; length up to 3.5 mm.

SILVANIDAE:

Sawtooth grain beetle, *Oryzaephilus surinamensis*
Foreign grain beetle, *Ahasversus advena*
Square-necked grain beetle, *Cathartus quadricollis*

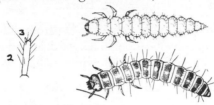

930. (908) Urogomphi movable, soft, 1-3 segmented (illust. 931).    931
Urogomphi fixed (not movable), hard (sclerotized), never segmented.    932

931. (930) Urogomphi usually 2 segmented.

HISTERIDAE

Urogomphi 1-3 segmented, often 3 segmented.

STAPHYLINIDAE

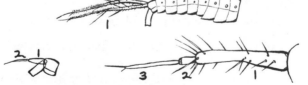

932. (930) Body clothed with fan-shaped, more or less flat hairs; white to pale; thorax about 2/3 the width of mid-abdomen; up to 2.5 mm.

ENDOMYCHIDAE: hairy cellar beetle,
*Mycetaea hirta*

Lacking fan-shaped hairs.    933

933. (932) Body dark brown, covered with long brown hairs; urogomphi in well-developed specimens, distinct, sharp-pointed;
tenth or end segment, large and forming a distinct, fused
sclerotized ring around the body.

DERMESTIDAE:
LARDER BEETLES, HIDE BEETLES    934

Not clothed with long brown hairs.                    940

934. (933) Urogomphi straight or nearly so from side view (illust.
933), except tip may be bent backward and downward.    935
Urogomphi curved from side view (illust. 937).         936

935. (934) Urogomphi straight from side view.

Black larder beetle,
*Dermestes ater (cadaverinus)*

Urogomphi straight with tip bent backward and downward.
*Dermestes nidum*

936. (934) Urogomphi curved backward and downward from side
view (illust. 937).                                    937
Urogomphi curved forward and upward (illust. 938).     938

937. (936) Head capsule with large conspicuous tubercles on each
side of front.

*Dermestes peruvianus*

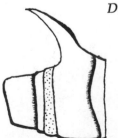

Head capsule lacking conspicuous tubercles.
Larder beetle, *Dermestes lardarius*

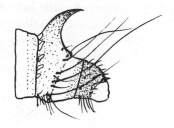

938. (936) Broad yellow median length-wise stripe above extending from the head to near the tip of body; head with conspicuous tubercles on front. 939

Yellow stripe lacking, or largely so.
*Dermestes undulatus* et al.

939. (938) Tibiae with 1 or 2 setae on apical (outer) margin of back face between long dorsal setae and ventral spine.
*Dermestes frischii*

Tibiae lacking such setae. Very common.
Hide beetle, *Dermestes maculatus*

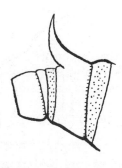

940. (933) Urogomphi directed up and outward (diverging), sharp pointed; head and thoracic segments above, dark brown, body white with flecks of lavender; up to 10 mm. Attack cured meats and similar animal products.

CORYNETIDAE:

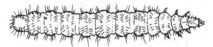

red-legged ham beetle, *Necrobia rufipes*

Not as above.                                                                941

941. (940) Urogomphi directed backward, with 2 spine-like projections near base of each urogomphus; head, and anal plate bearing urogomphi, rich amber brown; up to 10 mm. Infest ripe and dried fruit, grain and seeds.

NITIDULIDAE:

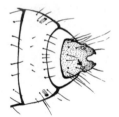 

dried fruit beetle, *Carpophilus hemipterus*
corn sap beetle, *Carpophilus dimidiatus*

Not as above.                                                                942

942. (941) Urogomphi prominent, brown, tips turned upward; head grayish white; thorax narrower than abdomen; up to 3.5-4 mm.

CUCUJIDAE: FLAT GRAIN BEETLES

Not as above.                                                                943

943. (942) Urogomphi sharp, upturned, dark brown; each body segment grayish (darker) above in central area; well-developed tubercles with long hairs on each side of darker areas; up to 8.5 mm.

EROTYLIDAE: *Pharaxonotha kirschii*

Not as above.                                                                944

944. (943) Elongate, somewhat flattened, dirty white; head, pronotum, and anal plate with urogomphi deep brown; urogomphi thick, rounded, with bluntly pointed tips; long colorless setae on all segments; up to 19 mm.

OSTOMMATIDAE:

cadelle, *Tenebroides mauritanicus*

Not as above. 945

945. (944) Mature larvae less than 6 mm. long. In moist situations and foods. (See adults for further identification.)

MYCETOPHAGIDAE, CRYPTOPHAGIDAE:
FUNGOUS BEETLES

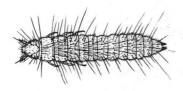 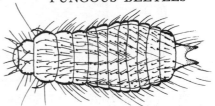

Mature larvae minute up to 32 mm. long. In dry cereal products and cereals (illust. 946).

TENEBRIONIDAE 946

946. (945) Very smooth, cylindrical, hard-bodied; yellowish to blackish brown; up to 32 mm.

Yellow mealworm, *Tenebrio molitor*
Dark mealworm, *Tenebrio obscurus*

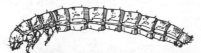

Much smaller, usually less than 10 mm.

Flour beetles, *Tribolium* spp. et al.

## HYMENOPTERA (Bees, Wasps and Ants)

947. (836) In paper nests, in soil, crevices, attached to structures, twigs and branches of shrubs and trees, or to rocks and cliffs; larvae stout, tapered near both ends; head small,

distinct; chewing mouthparts; thorax smaller than succeeding abdominal segments; 2 thoracic, 8 abdominal spiracles on each side. Social insects.

WASPS, HORNETS, and YELLOW JACKETS    595

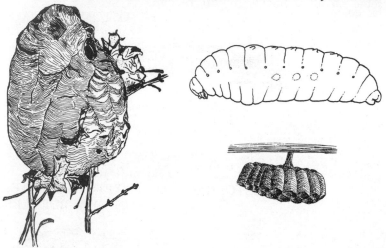

Not in paper nests.                                                      948

948. (947) In mud nests attached to structures, trees, rocks, or cliffs; larvae similar to above.

SPHECIDAE:
MUD DAUBERS, SOLITARY WASPS    594

Not in mud nests.                                                      949

949. (948) Nests in crevices, nail holes, burrows in wood, hollow or hollowed twigs, or in soil; larvae stout, pointed at head end; head non-sclerotized, small but inconspicuous; 2 thoracic and 8 abdominal spiracles on each side. Not social, but may be colonial.

APIDAE et al.: SOLITARY BEES

Not as above.                                                                950

950. (949) Nests with wax combs, exposed or concealed (illust. 951).                                                                951

Nests in soil, under rocks, in structures, wood, etc.; attended by wingless adults; larvae stout, more or less constricted near the center or forward of center of body, hind portion largest; head distinct but much smaller than thorax; mouth parts non-sclerotized; front end often turned back toward hind end. Winged males and females may be seen. Social insects.

FORMICIDAE: ANTS

951. (950) Nests of wax combs arranged in parallel, upright layers, usually above ground; in wall spaces, attics, hollow trees, rock cavities, etc., but may be attached to trees or to structures; large number of adults; larvae as in 950.

APIDAE: honey bee, *Apis mellifera*

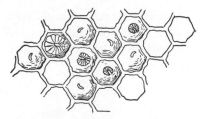

Nests with wax combs, usually in soil cavities, but may be in cavities above ground; combs not in parallel, upright layers (l, larval cluster; c, cocoons; h, honey); number of workers limited, usually less than 100.

BOMBIDAE: BUMBLE BEES

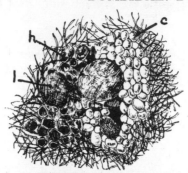

## DIPTERA (Flies)

952. (837) Aquatic, usually free swimming; head and thorax wider than abdomen, thorax widest; legs lacking; swim by repeated twisting of abdomen from side to side; usually with breathing tube near hind end of body. Wiggle tails.

Diptera: CULICIDAE, MOSQUITO LARVAE    953

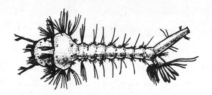

Not as above.    977

953. (952) Larvae rest flat against water surface when not in motion; apparently lacking or with short breathing tube only; palmate hairs on middle abdominal segments; never attached to roots or stems of plants.

*Anopheles* spp.    954

Larvae rest at 45° angle with water surface; breathing tube present, long; middle abdominal segments lack palmate hairs; some attached to roots and stems of plants, usually free swimming.    966

954. (953) Outer clypeal hairs simple, feathered or only sparsely branched.      955

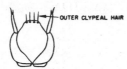 

Outer clypeal hairs densely branched.      959

955. (954) Outer clypeal hairs feathered or sparsely branched; antennal hairs many branched.      956

 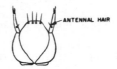

Inner clypeal hairs simple; antennal hair single or double.      957

956. (955) Outer and inner clypeal hairs equidistant at base; leaflets of abdominal palmate hairs, with smooth margins. Fresh and brackish water. Lower Rio Grande Valley, Texas, South Florida.

*Anopheles albimanus*

Outer clypeal hairs sparsely (5-10) branched on outer half, inner hairs simple or sparsely feathered; leaflets of abdominal palmate hairs with notched margins. Brackish water. Gulf and Atlantic coasts.

*Anopheles atropos*

957. (955) Antennae bare; frontal head hairs short and simple. Tree holes. Eastern United States to Nebraska and Texas.

*Anopheles barberi*

Antennae with spicules (spines); frontal head hairs long and branched.      958

958. (957) Posterior margin of spiracular plate with tails. Fresh water. South and West.

*Anopheles pseudopunctipennis*

Posterior margin of spiracular plate lacking tails. Fresh and salt water. Southwest and West.

*Anopheles franciscanus*

959. (954) Inner clypeal hairs separated by width of basal tubercles.          960

Inner clypeal hairs separated by less than width of basal tubercles.          961

960. (959) Occipital hairs with 5 or less branches; hair as shown on fourth abdominal segment usually single; brackish water. Atlantic and Gulf coasts.

*Anopheles bradleyi*

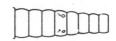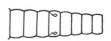

Occipital hairs with 6 or more branches; hairs as shown on fourth abdominal segment usually single, occasionally double. Fresh water. Eastern half of United States.

Common malaria mosquito,
*Anopheles quadrimaculatus*

961. (959) Three pairs of well-developed palmate hairs on fourth to sixth abdominal segments; hair as shown on fourth abdominal segment usually single. Southeastern United States.

Fresh water. *Anopheles georgianus*
Brackish water. *Anopheles bradleyi*

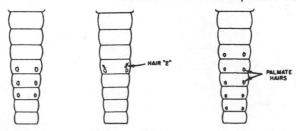

Five or 6 pairs of well-developed palmate hairs on second
or third to seventh abdominal segments.  962

962. (961) Hairs as indicated on fourth abdominal segment large
and multiple. Fresh water. Eastern United States to Canada.
*Anopheles crucians*

Hair as indicated on fourth abdominal segment small, single,
or wanting.  963

963. (962) Hair as indicated on fourth abdominal segment usually
simple.  964

Hair as indicated on fourth abdominal segment with 2 or
more branches.  965

964. (963) Inner clypeal hairs slightly feathered at tips. Tree holes
and artificial containers. Eastern United States.
*Anopheles walkeri*

 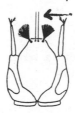

Inner clypeal hairs bare. Fresh water.
West Coast. *Anopheles occidentalis*
Widespread. *Anopheles punctipennis*

965. (963) Inner clypeal hairs typically forked or branched at tip;
hair as indicated on fourth abdominal segment usually multiple. Fresh water. Northern United States and Canada to
Alaska.

*Anopheles earlei*

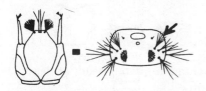 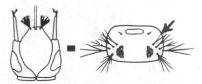

Inner clypeal hairs bare; hair as indicated on fourth abdominal segment usually double. Fresh water.
Widespread. *Anopheles punctipennis*
Western United States and Western Canada.
*Anopheles freeborni*

966. (953) Air tube with comb (pecten).      967

Air tube lacking comb.      972

967. (966) Air tube with several pairs of tufts or hairs.      968

Air tube with only 1 pair of tufts or hairs.      969

968. (967) Air tube lacking a basal pair of tufts, although several other tufts or hairs may be present.
*Culex* spp.

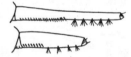

Air tube with a basal pair of hair tufts and a row of tufts or straight hairs.
*Culiseta* spp.

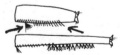

969. (967) Eighth abdominal segment with a plate bearing a row of teeth on hind side; head longer than wide; the common species with 4 stout head spines.
*Uranotaenia* spp.

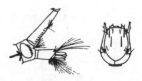

Eighth abdominal segment lacking a plate; head at least as wide as long, the hairs not spine-like.      970

970. (969) Anal segment completely ringed by a plate, which is pierced by tufts of median ventral brush.

*Psorophora* spp.

Anal segment not completely ringed by sclerotized plate, or, if ringed, median ventral brush posterior to plate.          971

971. (970) Head with lateral pouches.

*Deinocerites* spp.

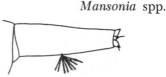

Head lacking lateral pouches.

*Aedes* spp.

972. (966) Air tube pointed and with teeth on 1 side.

*Mansonia* spp.

Air tube not pointed, lacking teeth.          973

973. (972) Eighth abdominal segment lacking comb scales, but with lateral plate bearing 2 spinulose hairs.

*Toxorhynchites* spp.

Eighth abdominal segment with comb scales; if lateral plate is present, it lacks hairs.          974

974. (973) Anal segment with median ventral brush; eighth abdominal segment with 2 rows of comb scales.

*Orthopodomyia* spp.

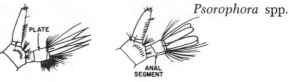

Anal segment lacking median ventral brush but with a pair of ventro-lateral tufts; eighth abdominal segment with only 1 row of comb scales.

*Wyeomyia* spp.

975. (834) Greater portion of body contacting water surface; air
tube short and flared; basal segments of abdomen closely appressed to head and thorax, small spines on side of abdomen.
*Anopheles* spp.

Smaller portion of body contacting water surface; basal
segment of abdomen not closely appressed to head and thorax.     976

976. (975) Air tube long and slender.

*Culex* spp.

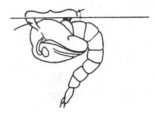

Air tube variable, but usually intermediate between *Anopheles* and *Culex* species.                          *Aedes* spp.

977. (952) Legless or having fleshy swellings (prolegs) only on
ventral side; elongate to slender; head capsule distinct or somewhat reduced; free living (illust. 978, 979).                    978

Legless; head much reduced; mandibles short and hook-like
(illust. 983 also), dark; body peg-shaped, anterior end pointed,
posterior end blunt.                                             983

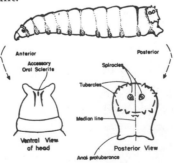

978. (977) Front half of body cylindrical, hind half enlarged and
club-shaped, the last segment with sucker-like disc for attach-
ment to rocks and other surfaces, the discs bearing a concen-
tric (common center) circle of bristles; head bears a pair of

fan-like organs for gathering food; rudimentary abdominal spiracles. Streams, often swift water.

SIMULIIDAE: BLACK FLIES

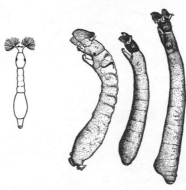

Not as above.                                                            979

979. (978) All or some dorsal segments above with narrow, sclerotized, strap-like transverse bands; last segment narrow, forming a short breathing tube; head narrower than succeeding segments; minute. Muck and wet environments, often in sewage beds and sink drains.

PSYCHODIDAE: DRAIN FLIES

Not as above.                                                            980

980. (979) Long and slender, white, consisting of apparently about 20 segments. Debris, in cracks and crevices.

SCENOPINIDAE:
window fly, *Scenopinus fenestralis*

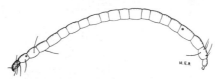

Body composed of 13 or less segments.                                    981

981. (980) Head small, pointed and retractile; body cylindrical, usually longitudinally lined; abdomen with a girdle of pseudopods on each segment. Mud under or near water to damp soil.

TABANIDAE:
HORSE and DEER FLIES

Head not retractile, about the size of body segments; body slender; 1 or more pseudopods on ventral surface.                 982

982. (981) With strong bristles or hairs on most segments, or only about 8 above on end of abdomen. Aquatic or terrestrial.
HELEIDAE: BITING MIDGES

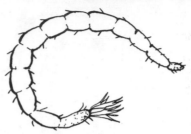

Aquatic; smooth or covered with fine soft hairs; last segment with a fine tuft of hairs on lower side.
CHIRONOMIDAE:
BLOOD WORMS, MIDGES

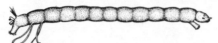

983. (977) Round (a) in cross section, tapering to a point anteriorly, blunt posteriorly.                                            985

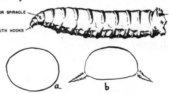

Flattened (b) in cross section, pointed anteriorly, rounded posteriorly; prominent lateral processes, sometimes dorsal also.
MUSCIDAE: *Fannia* spp.      984

984. (983) Lateral processes with numerous side branches (feathered). Manure, human excrement.
Latrine fly, *Fannia scalaris*

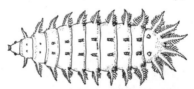

Lateral processes lacking numerous side branches. Manure, especially chicken.
Little house fly, *Fannia canicularis*

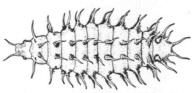

985. (983) Hind spiracles at end of short stalks (psp), which are in contact or joined at bases.

DROSOPHILIDAE:
FRUIT, VINEGAR, or POMACE FLIES

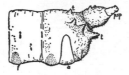 

Hind spiracles not on stalks, or only slightly raised, or even in a cavity. 986

986. (985) Spiracular plates smooth, or with at most 8 tubercles (illust. 985 t). 987

Spiracular plates surrounded by 10 or more tubercles (t).

CALLIPHORIDAE: BLOW FLIES 992

987. (986) Spiracular openings appear as 3 oblong openings close together; larvae in cured meats, cheeses, and similar foods.

CHLOROPIDAE: ham or cheese skipper,
*Piophila casei*

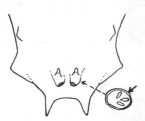 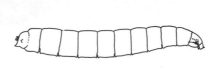

Spiracular openings kidney-shaped, or forming straight or sinuous (winding) slits.

MUSCIDAE 988

988. (987) Slits straight or nearly so. 989

Slits sinuous or kidney-shaped. 990

989. (988) Button of spiracular area (illust. 986 also) to the right of lower center (5 o'clock position).

Hydrotaea spp.

Button to right of middle center (3 o'clock position).

Ophyra spp.

990. (988) Slits kidney-shaped or occasionally in a bird's foot design.

False stable fly, *Muscina stabulans*

Slits sinuous.                                                                                      991

991. (990) Button marginal, attached to peritreme; peritreme distinct.

House fly, *Musca domestica*

Button in center, indistinct; entire spiracular area dark.

Stable fly, *Stomoxys stabulans*

992. (986) Peritreme complete.                                                     993

Peritreme incomplete.                                                                   996

993. (992) Accessory oral sclerite present.

*Cynomyopsis* spp., *Calliphora* spp.

Accessory oral sclerite absent.                                                    994

994. (993) Distance "A" distinctly less than "B."
*Phaenicia sericata*

Distance "A" approximately equal to "B."       995

995. (994) Peritreme not projecting between outer and middle slits.
*Phaenicia pallescens*

Peritreme projecting between outer and inner slits.
*Phaenicia caeruleiviridis*

996. (992) Tracheal trunks distinctly pigmented.
Screw-worm, *Callitroga hominivorax*

Tracheal trunks at most slightly pigmented.     997

997. (996) Spines on anal protuberance arranged in a "V" shape.
Secondary screw-worm, *Callitroga macellaria*

Spines on anal protuberance not arranged in a "V" shape.   998

998. (997) Inner slit directed away from middle line ventrally.
*Sarcophaga* spp.

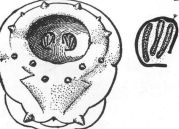

Inner slit directed toward the middle line ventrally.
*Phormia regina*

**1010.** (1) Hairs the only evidence of the organisms producing the damage.   1071

Evidence other than or in addition to hairs on or about damaged materials.  1011

**1011.** (1010) Either fecal stains or fecal pellets, or both, with or without loose hairs, as evidence of the organisms producing the damage.  1059

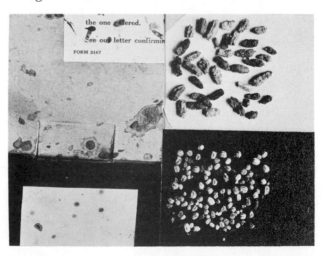

Evidence other than or in addition to fecal stains, fecal pellets, or hairs.  1012

1012. (1011) Tooth marks only, always in pairs; with or without either fecal stains, fecal pellets, or hairs (illust. 1072 also). 1042

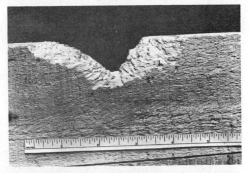

Evidence other than or in addition to above. 1013

1013. (1012) Foot prints in dust, soft foods, or other materials; with or without hairs, fecal pellets or stains, or tooth marks as evidence of the pest producing the damage. 1072

Evidence other than or in addition to above. 1014

1014. (1013) Rub (oil) marks or stains on wood (rafters) or other materials; with or without foot prints, hairs, fecal pellets or stains, or tooth marks as evidence of the pest producing the damage. 1072

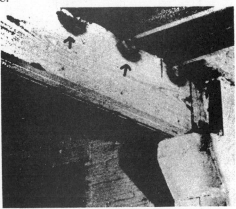

Evidence other than or in addition to above. 1015

1015. (1014) Damage to cellulose materials: wood, wood products, paper, wallpaper, cellophane, and similar materials, excluding fabrics. 1016

Damage to fabrics, yarns, felts, furs, hairs, hides, and feathers. 1045

1016. (1015) Burrows (engravings) (illust. 1017 upper) on rounded (unsawed) edges of boards or timbers, visible after bark is removed, do not extend into deep wood; attack occurred on dying and freshly dead timber with bark; exit holes often through bark (illust. 1023 upper); beetles may emerge from wood with bark in new structures, or from firewood. Do not continue infestations in structures. 1017

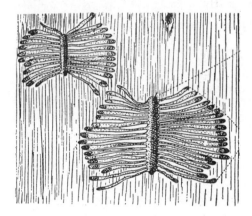

Burrows penetrate deeper into wood, or burrows largely within wood (illust. 1022 upper), *or* damage on or from exposed surfaces only of wood and other materials. 1019

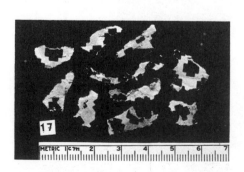

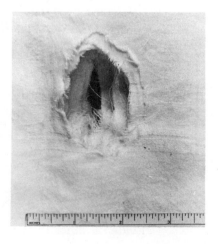

1017. (1016) Shallow oval pits or trenches in wood surfaces or inner bark up to about 14 mm. long, about 2-4 mm. wide, edges of burrows lacking notches or side burrows; round exit holes through bark. Do not attack wood in structures.

CURCULIONIDAE:
bark beetles, *Pissodes* spp. et al.

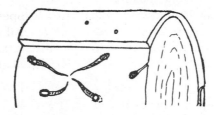

Burrows nearly always longer, often wider; often with notches or side burrows.                                        1018

1018. (1017) Engravings about 1.5-3.5 mm. wide; usually with notches (egg chambers) or side burrows (larval galleries) gradually increasing in diameter; leave attractive engravings on surface (illust. 1016 upper also).

SCOLYTIDAE:
BARK or ENGRAVER BEETLES

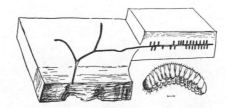

Burrows larger and longer, meandering and often running together forming broad feeding areas; often packed tightly with granular frass. Beetles may emerge, especially from firewood.

Burrows broadly oval, CERAMBYCIDAE:
ROUND-HEADED BORERS
Burrows narrowly oval, BUPRESTIDAE:
FLAT-HEADED BORERS

1019. (1016) Burrows hidden, often broadening into chambers in wood, seldom or never reaching surface, except by accident, so as to expose burrows; when reaching surface covered tubes lead from openings (illust. 1020), *or* occasional small holes about 2 mm. in diameter for extrusion of pellets, many of which have been plugged with pellets, reaching surface from larger cavities beneath (illust. 1022); burrows produced by ingestion (eating) of wood; hairs, paired tooth marks, and fecal stains on surface scarce or absent.

ISOPTERA: TERMITES 1020

Openings of burrows normally exposed at surface for passage of insects or extrusion of frass or pellets (illust. 1025), *or* damage on or from surface only; hairs, paired tooth marks (illust. 1012), fecal pellets or stains may be evident on or about damaged materials (illust. 1023 lower). 1023

1020. (1019) Many burrows lined with excrement and earth cemented together; burrows penetrate soil or surrounding woodwork or are connected with soil by tubes of earth and excrement.

Subterranean termites,
*Reticulitermes flavipes* 263

Burrows not lined with earth and excrement cemented together; usually not entering soil, but often entering wood or other cellulose materials (illust. 1021). 1021

1021. (1020) Burrows in dry sound wood, often enlarged into chambers with conspicuous connecting burrows; dry pellets drop from infested wood (illust. 1022). 1022

Burrows in damp rotten wood, largely forming lamellate layers corresponding to annual ring growth; larger fecal pellets about 1.4-1.8 mm. long, 0.8 mm. wide, cylindrical, ends rounded, color usually yellow to brown, 6 distinct longitudinal ridges or lines; some burrows with pellet dams formed by fastening pellets together with liquid feces or saliva.

Rotten wood termites. *Zootermopsis* spp.    258

1022. (1021, 1031, 1070) Conspicuous connecting burrows directed more or less across the grain of the wood, about 2 mm. in diameter, these small burrows often reaching the wood surface, but the majority plugged with frass at any one observation; larger fecal pellets about 1 mm. long and 0.6 mm. wide, cylindrical, ends rounded, usually yellow to dull red or brown in color, 6 distinct longitudinal ridges.

Dry wood termites, *Kalotermes* spp.    261

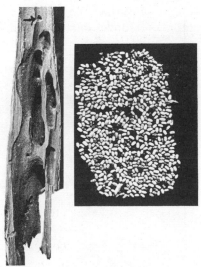

Wood reduced to fine powdery consistency; tiny pellets, much finer than above, drop from infested wood; disposal holes, many plugged with frass, smaller than above; frequently in furniture and other movable materials, never outdoors. Southern Florida and Louisiana.

Powder post or furniture termites,
*Cryptotermes brevis, C. cavifrons*    260

1023. (1019) Smooth (shot) holes, *or* burrows chewed or eaten in or through materials; usually in wood, sometimes in paper products; occasionally scattered small holes about 2 mm. in diameter, many of which have been plugged with frass (illust. 1022 upper also). 1024

Holes at surface more or less irregular in outline, leading to interior cavities or chambers (illust. 1025, 1039), *or* feeding and chewing from surface or edges of materials only; paper and materials of similar texture often much torn. 1039

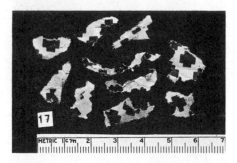

1024. (1023) Wood not ingested (eaten), the frass retaining the original character of wood; burrows may be empty or filled with frass, frass if present, resembling sawdust, sometimes shredded resembling excelsior. 1025

Wood ingested, fecal remains have lost their original wood character; burrows usually but not always filled. 1029

1025. (1024) One or more openings reaching surface of solid or rotten wood; interior hollowed to form anastomosing chambers; chambers or burrows not lined with excrement and earth cemented together; slender bits of wood up to about 3 mm. in length containing many insect parts, including ants, deposited outside or beneath openings, or smaller accumulations at bottoms of cavities in wood or other materials (illust. 1039 also).

FORMICIDAE:
carpenter ants, *Camponotus* spp.     637

Burrows round to broadly oval; wood lacking hollowed out chambers.     1026

1026. (1025) Frass (bits of wood) resembling sawdust; burrows round.     1027

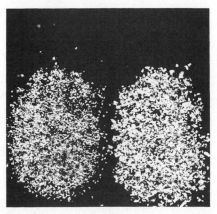

Frass shredded, resembling excelsior, near openings; granular ingested frass packed tightly in burrows; burrows broadly oval in outline (illust. 1035 also).

CERAMBYCIDAE:
ROUND-HEADED BORERS    418

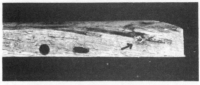

1027. (1026) Holes in rotten or very soft wood, often numerous, 3-5 mm. in diameter; bees smaller than honey bees, often seen entering and leaving burrows, colonial, not social.

Small carpenter bees, *Ceratina* spp.    593

Holes in solid twigs or trunks of living trees, or firm dead wood or lumber and houses; larger than above, up to 13 mm. (1/2 inch) wide (illust. 1028). 1028

1028. (1027) Holes in weathered wood in trees or structures; frass glued together to form partitions across burrows, separating it into a series of chambers; burrows about 13 mm. wide;

frass from burrows coarse, resembling sawdust; bees resemble bumble bees.

Large carpenter bees, *Xylocopa* spp.   592

Silk webbing in burrows mixed with frass (illust. 1032 also).  Widespread.

LEPIDOPTERA:
wood-boring caterpillars, carpenter worms,
*Prionoxystus* spp., leopard moth, *Zeuzera pyrina*

1029. (1024) Burrows round, uniform in diameter, not packed with frass; surrounding wood usually with bluish or black stain; burrows often lined with spongy or hardened coating; beetles attack dying trees and newly cut logs; exit holes about 3 mm. or less in diameter (illust. 1018 upper).

SCOLYTIDAE:
AMBROSIA BEETLES

Burrows never surrounded by stained wood; spongy coating lacking.   1030

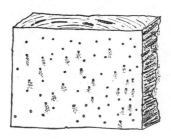

**1030.** (1029) Fecal pellets in frass round, elliptical or cylindrical; not powdery. **1031**

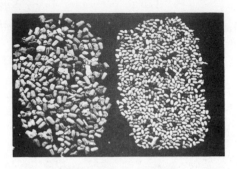

Frass fine or powdery, *or* coarse, resembling sawdust. **1033**

**1031.** (1030) Round holes about 2 mm. in diameter, many of which may be plugged with frass pellets, frcm which cylindrical pellets about 1 mm. in diameter and 0.6 mm. wide, with 6 distinct longitudinal ridges, are extruded at intervals; these small holes lead to large chambers within wood.

Dry wood termites, *Kalotermes* spp. **1022**

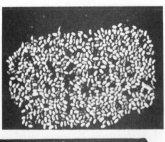

Pellets round or elliptical; burrows round in outline. **1032**

1032. (1031) Pellets mixed with silk webbing or threads. Widespread.

LEPIDOPTERA:
Carpenter worms, *Prionoxystus* spp.
Leopard moth, *Zeuzera pyrina*

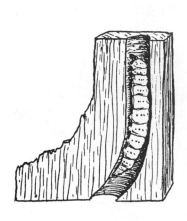
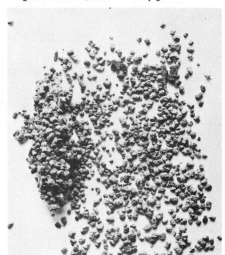

Pellets not mixed with silk threads, smaller than above, tend to be elongate with ends rounded.

ANOBIIDAE:
*Anobium* spp., *Nicobium* spp.   437

1033. (1030) Frass coarse, resembling sawdust, tightly packed in burrows.   1034
Frass very fine, *or* a coarse powder (illust. 1030 lower).   1035

1034. (1033) Unseasoned or moist logs or wood when attacked; burrows round. Largely in fire wood.

SIRICIDAE:
horntails, *Tremex* spp., *Sirex* spp.

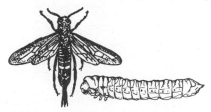

Wet or very moist wood when attacked, usually below soil surface; burrows broadly oval; frass packed in burrows.

OEDEMERIDAE:
wharf borer, *Nacerda melanura*

1035. (1033) Frass tightly packed in burrows, resembling coarse powder or granules, does not break apart readily, but may do so and sift from burrows on jarring; shredded non-ingested wood may be near openings (illust. 1018 also).

Burrows broadly oval,
CERAMBYCIDAE: ROUND-HEADED BORERS    418
Burrows narrowly oval,
BUPRESTIDAE: FLAT-HEADED BORERS    432

Frass fine and loose, powdery, readily sifts from burrows on jarring; wood often riddled with holes, at least near surface; burrows oval or round (illust. 1036).    1036

1036. (1035) Burrows broadly oval, in dry wood, especially sapwood; frass powdery, very fine, with tiny cylindrical pellets, frass sifts freely from wood on jarring; wood riddled, often reduced to a powdery mass, often in old buildings and lumber.
CERAMBYCIDAE: old house borer,
*Hylotrupes bajulus*

Burrows round, usually smaller than above.    1037

1037. (1036) Frass very fine and loose, resembling talcum powder in fineness; in newly seasoned sapwood; exit holes about 0.8-1.6 mm. wide.
LYCTIDAE: lyctus powder post beetles,
*Lyctus* spp. et al.    446

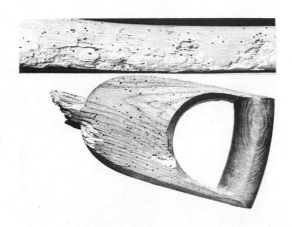

Frass fine and loose, resembling coarse powder, pellets often distinguishable in frass (illust. 1030 lower right also).

Other POWDER POST BEETLES   1038

1038. (1037) Exit holes about 3.2 mm. or more wide; egg tunnels of adults free of frass; larval tunnels filled with frass, which tends to stick together (cakes), often brownish because of ingested bark.

BOSTRICHIDAE   452

Exit holes about 0.8-3.2 mm. wide; burrows filled with fine to coarse loose powdery frass, often containing tiny pellets, frass sifts freely from burrows.

PTINIDAE and ANOBIIDAE:
pellets elongate, *Xestobium* spp., *Anobium* spp., *Nicobium* spp.;   436
pellets round and flattened, *Hadrobregmus* spp.   437

1039. (1023) Damage to wood largely from the interior; one or more irregular holes or crevices reaching surface through which insects pass, or discard slender bits of wood up to about 3 mm. long, containing many insect parts, including ants, deposited outside or beneath openings, or similar accumulations at bottom of cavities in wood or other materials (illust. 1025 also).

FORMICIDAE:
carpenter ants, *Camponotus* spp.    637

Damage to wood and other materials produced by chewing and feeding largely from surface (illust. 1016).    1040

1040. (1039) Feeding damage at edges, corners, and folds, usually penetrating thin materials; paper and materials of similar texture frequently torn (illust. 1016); paired tooth marks on wood (illust. 1012) or paper (illust. 1071) often plainly visible (illust. 1041) upper also).    1041

Damage largely due to feeding or chewing on surface, often not penetrating materials; materials other than wood (illust. 1042 lower).    1043

1041. (1040) Damage to bark and cambium layer of woody plants outdoors, below snow line, sometimes to roots also; tooth marks in pairs showing on wood or in bark. Yard pests.

Field vole or meadow mouse,
*Microtus* spp. et al.    79

Damage other than to growing plants outdoors.      1042

1042. (1012, 1041) Tooth marks, when present, in pairs, about 1
mm. or more wide, producing irregularities on chewed or
torn edges; paper frequently torn (illust. 1016); larger fecal
pellets nearly 5 mm., usually more, up to 20 mm. in length;
hairs on or about damaged materials.

RODENTS  1061

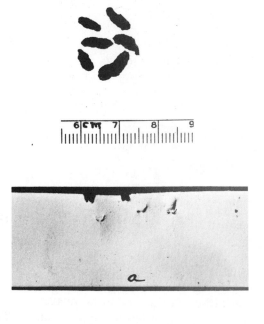

Mandible marks or scratches from mandibles along chewed edges frequently visible with magnification only, much finer than above, not in pairs; little or no tearing; larger fecal pellets smaller, nearly always less than 5 mm. long; fecal stains often present; hairs lacking.

INSECTS: ROACHES, CRICKETS, etc.    1059

1043. (1040) Minute shiny or iridescent scales on damaged materials, often visible as flecks of light, not readily visible without magnification.

THYSANURA: SILVERFISH    1044

No scales on or about damaged materials.    1044

1044. (1043) Material thinned by feeding from surface, which is slightly roughened or pitted from uneven feeding and removal of material; edge damage largely a result of surface feeding.

THYSANURA: SILVERFISH    1059

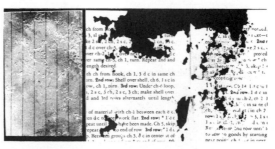

Surface roughened from chewing and feeding, the roughness produced by the cellulose fibers being pulled or picked loose while feeding, sometimes forming an irregular matted network over surface as a result of chewing on pulled surface fibers.

ORTHOPTERA: ROACHES and CRICKETS 1059

1045. (1015) Silk tubes and cases, *or* burrows lined with silk, in or on damaged materials; sometimes portable silk cases (illust. 1047) some distance away; hairs of furs cut at or near base exposing bare hide; barbules only of feathers eaten.

LEPIDOPTERA: CLOTHES MOTHS 1046

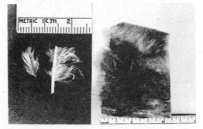

No traces of silk in or on damaged materials. 1049

1046. (1045, 1065) Silk cases portable, usually containing larvae when on damaged materials (illust. 1047). 1047

Attached silk tubes and webs on or in damaged materials (illust. 1048); fecal pellets 0.5 mm. or less in diameter, frequently mixed with webbing. 1048

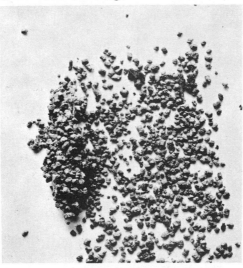

1047. (1046) Portable cases much enlarged in central portion.

Plaster bagworm, *Tineola walsinghami*    567

Cases cigar-shaped, slightly enlarged in central portion; cases often some distance away, usually above damaged materials, empty, containing pupae or pupal cases. Fabric, unless thick and loosely woven, damaged on surface only; if loosely woven, cases and burrows may be in fabric.

Casemaking clothes moth, *Tinea pellionella*    569

1048. (1046) Silk tubes and webs flimsy and discontinuous; largely surface damage; tubes may enter thick loose materials.

Webbing clothes moth, *Tineola bisselliella*    566

Silk lined burrows in materials  uniform in thickness and continuous; occasionally attached tubes or loose portable tubes on surface.

Carpet moth, *Trichophaga tapetzella*   561

1049. (1045) Damaged materials are fabrics, yarns, felts, etc.   1050
   Damaged materials are furs, hides, feathers, etc.   1056

1050. (1049) Threads damaged: pulled (a), looped, or broken (b); if broken, ends tapered or frayed; one or several threads damaged with no traces of damage to neighboring threads.
MECHANICAL DAMAGE

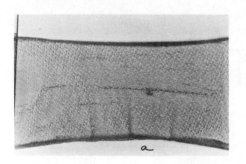 

Damage other than above.   1051

1051. (1050) Round or irregular holes that partially or completely penetrate fabric; surface or ends of individual threads around margins of holes brown or black from charring. In worn or washed materials, charring is not readily visible without magnification, sometimes entirely removed.
BURNS

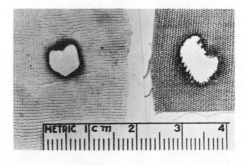

Damage other than above.   1052

**1052.** (1051) Damage produced by repeated feeding on surface, often penetrating thin fabrics; holes usually less than about 6-10 mm. in diameter, unless damage is extensive, surface damage surrounding holes; fecal pellets on or about damaged materials, less than 1 mm. in greatest dimension. 1053

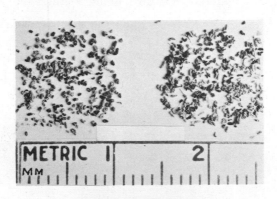

Large irregular holes penetrating fabric, lacking surrounding surface damage, or surface much torn; many holes more than 8 mm. in diameter; fecal pellets small to large. 1054

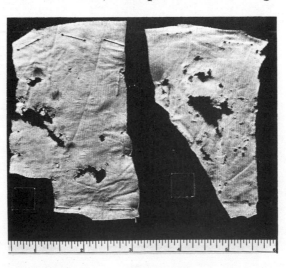

1053. (1052) Minute shiny or iridescent scales on damaged materials, often visible as flecks of light, not readily visible without magnification; synthetic or starch-sized fibers or fabrics only (illust. 1052 upper also).

THYSANURA: SILVERFISH 1059

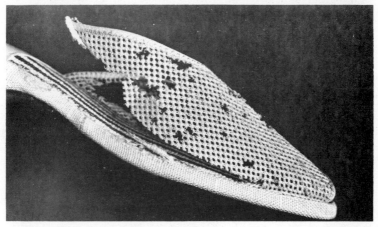

Pile frequently eaten away often penetrating fabric; much surface damage; wool and silk fibers and fabric only (illust. 1058 also).

COLEOPTERA: CARPET BEETLES 1059

1054. (1052) Large irregular holes chewed or torn in fabric, often much torn, holes may be 25 mm. or more in diameter, edges

frayed; damage may penetrate a number of layers (illust. 1016 lower); larger fecal pellets nearly 5 mm., usually more, up to 20 mm. in length; hairs often present.

RODENTS 1061

Irregular holes, usually much smaller than above, on exposed surfaces only; edges frayed or smooth, never torn; larger fecal pellets less than 5 mm. long; hairs absent (illust. 1052, 1053). 1055

1055. (1054) Irregular holes variable in size, largely at edges or folds of fabric, unless damage is extensive (illust. 1052 lower).

ORTHOPTERA: CRICKETS 1059

Irregular holes in any exposed portion of fabric. 1059

1056. (1049) Skin or hide badly damaged, often loosening and freeing patches of fur; relatively small amount of hair cut without damaging hide; feeding among feathers largely along basal portion of shaft on adhering skin and skin scales (illust. 1057).

COLEOPTERA:
HIDE and CABINET BEETLES 1057

Skin or hide not at all or only slightly damaged; large amounts of hair damaged, in extreme cases bare hide left with relatively little hide damage (illust. 1058); hairs of hair products (brushes) cut off or nibbled along edges; feeding among feathers on barbules largely, in extreme cases only the bare shafts remain.

COLEOPTERA: CARPET BEETLES 1058

1057. (1056) Hide damaged chiefly on inner surface which becomes exposed to insects by larvae penetrating hide or through openings in lining, etc.; hair loosened by hide destruction from inner surface; cast skins on damaged materials dark brown in color, each segment clothed with numerous brown hairs, 2 sharply pointed straight or curved spines near posterior end; fecal pellets long and slender, 0.5-3 mm. long, 0.2 mm. wide.

COLEOPTERA:
hide beetles, *Dermestes* spp.    464

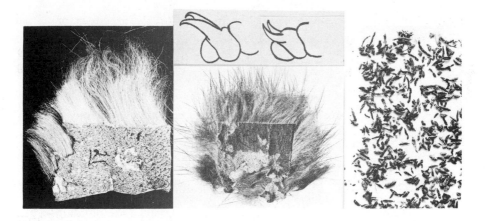

Hide damaged chiefly on outer surface by larvae penetrating fur and feeding on hide at base of hairs; hairs loosened from hide by destruction of hide from outer surface; cast skins on damaged materials light brown in color, a mass of rust-brown hairs on posterior segments; fecal pellets globular or elliptical, larger pellets about 0.3 mm. long, 0.2 mm. wide.

COLEOPTERA:
cabinet beetles, *Trogoderma* spp.    503

1058. (1056, 1065) Primary damage produced by hairs being cut or eaten off near base, leaving hide bare; patches of loose long hairs frequently containing brown larval skins; microscopically the loose and attached guard or coarse hairs show much more feeding damage toward the basal end among the pelage hairs than at distal end; fecal pellets (illust. 1065 lower) 0.25 mm. or less in diameter

Black carpet beetle, *Attagenus piceus*    494

Primary damage produced by tips of hairs being cut or eaten off leaving an uneven fur surface; loose bits of hairs relatively short; in advanced cases of damage patches of fur eaten away leaving hide bare, or with patches of attached shortened hairs; microscopically the guard or coarse hairs showing much more feeding damage near the tips than deeper among the inner pelage hairs; larval skins on damaged materials covered with nearly black hairs; fecal pellets 0.25 mm. or less in diameter (illust. 1065 lower).

Carpet beetles, *Anthrenus* spp.    501

1059. (1011, 1042, 1044, 1053, 1055) Dark colored stains from liquid feces on damaged materials, stained areas often with a thin deposit of solid materials; larger fecal pellets, when present, less than 5 mm. long; hairs absent (illust. 1060).    1060

Fecal stains lacking, fecal pellets on or about damaged materials; hairs often present.    1061

1060. (1059) Majority of stains ranging up to 5-10 mm. in widest portion; larger fecal pellets on or about damaged materials 2.5-4.5 mm. long, color usually gray to black; large smoother pellets with 6 more or less distinct longitudinal ridges (illust. 1062: 2, 3, 5; 1072: 7 also).

ORTHOPTERA: LARGER ROACHES    217

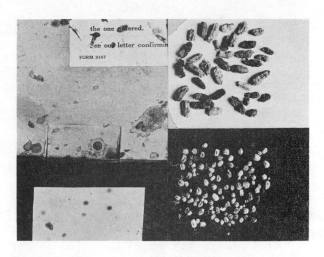

Stains largely ranging from 1-4 mm. in widest portion, occasional stains larger; large smoother fecal pellets with 6 more or less distinct longitudinal ridges, 1.5 mm. or less in length (illust. 1062: 4, 6; 1072: 8 also).

ORTHOPTERA: SMALLER ROACHES    213, 1061

1061.  (1042, 1054, 1059) Larger fecal pellets (illust. 1072: 1-6) on or about damaged materials about 5-20 mm. in length, if less than 5 mm. long, the smoother pellets always lack longitudinal ridges (see couplet 1062); tooth marks if present on damaged materials, in pairs; hairs (illust. 1075) on or about damaged materials; *or* fecal pellets composed entirely of easily recognizable insect parts.    1071

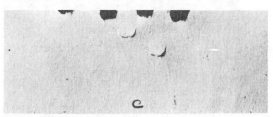

Larger fecal pellets less than 5 mm. in length; hairs absent (illust. 1062).    1062

1062.  (1061) Larger fecal pellets (2, 3, 5) on or about damaged materials 2.5-4.5 mm. long, color usually gray to black; large

smoother pellets with 6 more or less distinct longitudinal
ridges (illust. 1060 upper pellets; 1072: 7 also).
ORTHOPTERA: LARGER ROACHES    217

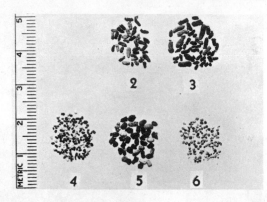

Larger fecal pellets about 2.5 mm. or less in length (4, 6)
(illust. 1060 lower pellets also).        1063


1063. (1062) Larger fecal pellets 0.9 mm. or less in length (illust.
1064, 1065).        1064
Larger fecal pellets 0.9 to about 2.5 mm. in length.        1066


1064. (1063) Larger fecal pellets 0.6-0.9 mm. long, usually slender,
rough and curled or twisted.
THYSANURA: SILVERFISH    206

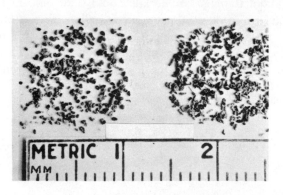

Larger fecal pellets 0.5 mm. or less in length, largely
globular or elliptical, few slender, smooth (illust. 1065).    1065


1065. (1064) Silk webbing mixed with pellets (a).
LEPIDOPTERA: CLOTHES MOTHS    1046

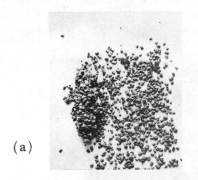

(a)  (b)

Silk webbing or threads lacking (b).

COLEOPTERA: carpet beetles,
*Attagenus* spp., *Anthrenus* spp.  1058

1066. (1063) Pellets entirely or almost lacking longitudinal ridges, larger pellets 1.5-2.5 mm. long (illust. 1067).

ORTHOPTERA: CRICKETS  1067

Large smooth fecal pellets with 6 more or less distinct longitudinal ridges, 1.5 mm. or less in length.  1069

1067. (1066) Larger fecal pellets about 2-2.5 mm. long, about 1.25-1.5 mm. wide; largely accidental in houses.

Large field crickets, *Gryllus* spp.  242

Larger fecal pellets about 1.5-2.5 mm. long, less than 1.25 mm. wide.  1068

1068. (1067) Larger fecal pellets about 2-2.5 mm. long, about 1 mm. wide.

House cricket, *Acheta domestica*  241

Larger fecal pellets about 1.5-2 mm. long, about 0.75 mm. wide; largely accidental in houses.

Small field crickets, *Nemobius* spp.  242

1069. (1066) Larger fecal pellets about 0.9-1.1 mm. long, globular to elliptical (illust. 1072: 8 also).

Brown-banded roach, *Supella supellectillium*     215

Larger fecal pellets about 1-1.5 mm. long, cylindrical.     1070


1070. (1069) Larger fecal pellets 1-1.5 mm. long, white to black and variable in colors (a).

German roach, *Blattella germanica*     216

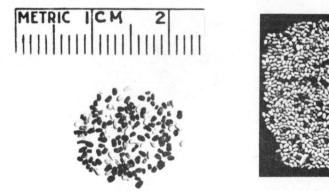

(a)                           (b)

Larger fecal pellets about 1 mm long, usually yellow to dull red or brown and uniform in color; extruded from wood near-by or above (b).

Dry wood termites, *Kalotermes* spp.     1022


1071. (1010, 1061) Hairs on or about damaged materials (illust. 1075); insect parts in pellets scarce; pairs of tooth marks often present on damaged materials (illust. 1012 also).     1072

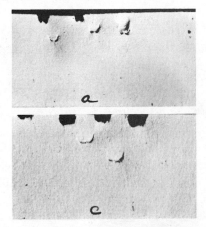

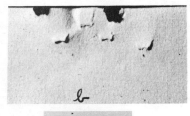

Hairs absent; fecal pellets often the only evidence of the presence of pests, usually in attics, open basements or sheds, often in piles, crumble readily with pressure when dry; composed entirely of easily recognizable insect parts.

CHIROPTERA: BATS     52

1072. (1013, 1014, 1071) Coarse or guard hairs about 10-12 mm. or less in length; larger fecal pellets about 4-9 mm. long, 1-3 mm. wide (5, 6); pairs of tooth marks (illust. 1012, 1071a) about 0.8-1.4 mm. wide; foot prints (illust. 1073) about 17-22 mm. or less from heel to tip of longest toe of hind feet; rub marks (illust. 1074), when visible, much smaller than below.

HOUSE and DEER MICE:
*Mus musculus, Peromyscus* spp. et al.     79

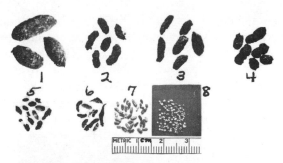

Coarse or guard hairs (illust. 1076, 1077) about 10-30 mm. in length; larger fecal pellets 5-20 mm. long, 2 mm. or more wide (1, 4); pairs of tooth marks (illust. 1012, 1071) about 1.6-3.5 mm. wide; foot prints (illust. 1073) 25 mm. or more from heel to tip of longest toe of hind feet; rub marks (illust. 1074) often conspicuous on wood (rafters) or other surfaces, much larger than possible for mice.

LARGER RODENTS     1073

1073. (1072) Hairs fine and silky, lacking alternate light and dark bands, up to 15-20 mm. long; pairs of tooth marks about 1.6 mm. wide; larger fecal pellets up to 6-12 mm. long, 2-4 mm. wide; foot prints up to 29-36 mm. from heel to tip of longest toe of hind feet.

FLYING SQUIRRELS:
*Glaucomys volans, G. sabrinus*    73

Hairs coarser, not silky; foot prints usually larger to much larger from heel to tip of longest toe of hind feet; larger fecal pellets about 5-20 mm. long, 2.5-6 mm. wide; tooth marks from about 1.7-3.5 mm. wide.    1074

1074. (1073) Coarse or guard hairs (illust. 1076) with alternate light and dark bands; pairs of tooth marks (illust. 1071b) about 1.7-3.5 mm. wide; larger fecal pellets up to about 15 mm. long, 6.5 mm. wide; foot prints up to 25-85 mm. from heel to tip of longest toe of hind feet.

CHIPMUNKS and SQUIRRELS    1075

Coarse or guard hairs (illust. 1077) lacking alternate light and dark bands, color varying from light to dark from base to tips of hairs; pairs of tooth marks (illust. 1071) up to 2-2.5 mm. wide; larger fecal pellets (illust. 1072: 1-3) up to 20 mm. long; foot prints (illust. 1073) up to 44 mm. from heel to tip of longest toe of hind feet; rub marks often conspicuous on wood (rafters) or other surfaces.

RATS    1077

1075. (1074) Coarse or guard hairs up to 10-12 mm. long; larger fecal pellets up to 5-11 mm. long, 2.5-3.5 mm. wide; tooth marks 1.7-2.3 mm. wide; foot prints up to 30-38 mm. from heel to tip of longest toe of hind feet.

CHIPMUNKS:
*Eutamias* spp. & *Tamias* spp.     71

Coarse or guard hairs up to 30 mm. long; larger fecal pellets about 7-15 mm. long, 3-6.5 mm. wide; tooth marks 2-3.5 mm. wide; foot prints 44 mm. or more in length from heel to tip of longest toe of hind feet.

TREE SQUIRRELS   1076

1076. (1075) Light bands on coarse or guard hairs decidedly rufous (red) in color, dark bands narrow, 2 mm. or less in width; pairs of tooth marks 2-2.5 mm. wide; larger fecal pellets (illust. 1072) up to 11 mm. long, 4 mm. wide; foot prints up to about 44-48 mm. from heel to tip of longest toe of hind feet.

RED SQUIRRELS:
*Sciurus hudsonicus*     76

Light bands on coarse or guard hairs white to yellow, dark bands 2-5 mm. wide; pairs of tooth marks (illust. 1071b) 2.5-3.5 mm. wide; larger fecal pellets (illust. 1072) up to 15 mm. long, 6 mm. wide; foot prints up to 60-85

mm. or more in length from heel to tip of longest toe of hind
feet.

1077. (1074) Coarse or guard hairs light brown to black, frequently
   lighter in color at the basal portion; larger fecal pellets
   (illust. 1072: 2-3) about 11 mm. or less in length, 3-4 mm.
   wide; pairs of tooth marks (illust. 1071) (b).

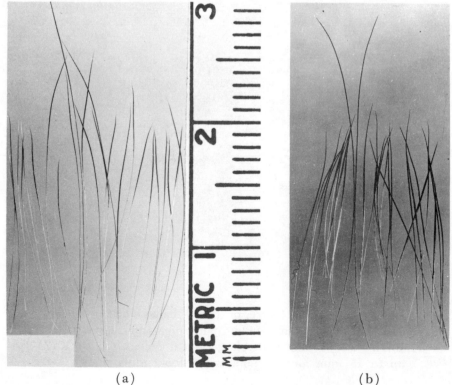

(a)                                                 (b)

about 2-2.5 mm. wide; foot prints up to 33-39 mm. from heel to tip of longest toe of hind feet (a).

BLACK or ROOF RAT:
*Rattus rattus*     81

Coarse or guard hairs largely light brown to brown, frequently gray to white on basal portion; larger fecal pellets (illust. 1072: 1) 9-20 mm. long, 3-6 mm. wide; pairs of tooth marks (illust. 1071c) about 2.5 mm. wide; foot prints (illust. 1073) up to 38-44 mm. from heel to tip of largest toe of hind feet (b).

BROWN or HOUSE RAT:
*Rattus norvegicus*     81

# INDEX

## DIRECTORY OF COMMON NAMES

(See CONTENTS for taxonomic names)

pigeon 51
purple martin 49
robin 50-51
sapsucker 46
starling 49, 51
swallow 48-49
woodpecker 46
Biting midge 692, 982
Blood worm(s) 982
Body lice 283
Book lice 189, *264-273*, see psocids also
  book 265
  dark 267
  larger pale 268
  reticulate winged 267
  spotted-winged 268
Borer(s) 385, 411, 412, *415-455, 891-907,
  1018-1039*
  european furniture 441
  flatheaded 385, *432-433*, 905, 1018,
    1035
  large grain 530, 900
  lead cable 455
  lesser grain 530, 900
  long-horned 411-412, *416-431, 905-907,*
    1018, 1026, 1035
  old house 427, 907, 1036
  round headed, see long horned
  wharf 411, 418, 904, 1034
  wood 385, 404, 411-412, *415-455*, 891-
    892, 896-899, 903-907, 1023-1039
Bug(s) 183, 195, *342-369*
  bed 343-352
  boxelder 356
  conenose 354, *357-368*
  pill 7, 21-22
  sow 7, 21-22
  squash 356
Burn(s) 1051

Cadelle 464, 944
Capsules 3, 830, *840-850*
Carnivore(s) 54
Cast skins 1
Caterpillar(s) 3, 831, 832, *860-884*, 1028,
  1032
Centipede(s) 5, 8-11
  house 9
Chameleon 38
Cheese skipper 701, 987
Chigger(s) 125, 152
Chipmunk(s) 66, *70-71*
Cluster fly 711
Cockroach(es) 188, 197, 209, *211-240*, 841,
  1042, 1044, 1060-1062, 1069-1070
  american 230, 238, 848, 1060-1062
  australian 226, 238, 239, 850, 1060-1062
  brown 230, 240, 850, 1060-1062
  brown-banded 215, 234, 236, 845, 1069
  capsule(s) 3, *840-850*
  cuban 217

egg parasite 381, 411
field 216
german 216, 234, 235, 846, 1070
lobster 220, 225
madeira 224, 232, 843
oriental 221, 237, 848, 1060-1062
parasite 381, 411
smoky brown 229, 238, 240, 849, 1060-
  1062
spotted mediterranean 213, 232, 845,
  1060
wood 214, 222, 229, 846
Cocoon(s) 839, *853-855*
Copperhead snake 41
Coral snake 43
Cricket(s) 188, 197, 209, 210, *241-250*,
  1042, 1044, 1055, 1066-1068
  cave 210,
  house 241, 1068
  large field *242-247*, 1067
  small field 242, *248-250*, 1068

Daddy-long-legs 7, 23-24
Damaged material(s) 1, *1010-1075*, *see*
  Secondary signs also
  burns 1051
  fabrics, etc. 1015, *1049-1056*
  feathers 1015, 1049, *1056-1058*
  furs 1015, 1049, *1056-1058*
  hides 1015, 1049, *1056-1058*
  mechanical 1050
  paper, etc. 1015 *1039-1044*
  wood 1012, *1015-1041*

Egg(s), see insect
Earwig(s) 184, 192, *256-257*
Eye gnat(s) 701

Fabric(s), see Damaged materials
Feather(s), see Damged materials
Fecal pellet(s), see Secondary evidence
Fecal stain(s), see Secondary evidence
Firebrat(s) 178, 207
Flea(s) 182, *655-675*, 830, 835, 855
  bat 657
  bird 668, 669
  cat 675
  chigoe 661
  cocoon 855
  dog 675
  european chicken 669
  fowl 668, 669
  human 663
  mouse 670, 672
  northern rat 668
  oriental rat 663
  rabbit 665
  rat 662, 633, 666, 667, 668, 672, 673
  snow 200
  squirrel 666, 667
  sticktight 661
  western chicken 669

malaria 739, 960
northern house 822
pupae 3, 834, *975-976*
salt marsh 771, 776
southern house 772
yellow fever 772
Moth(s) 193, *557-580*, 831-832, 854, 857,
    *860-884*, 1028, 1032, 1045-1048, 1065
  almond 580, 883
  angoumois grain 565, 860, 864, 875
  brown house 562, 872
  carpenter 1028, 1032
  carpet 561, 873, 1048
  casemaking clothes 569, 871, 1047
  clothes 561, 562, 566, 567, 569, 1045-
    1048, 1065
  clover hayworm 571
  cocoons 853-854
  european grain 564, 875
  families *557-558*, *860-866*
  indian meal 575, 878
  leopard 1028, 1032
  meal 573, 877
  mediterranean flour 578, 884
  pink corn worm 559, 866
  plaster bagworm 567, 871, 1047
  pupae 853-854
  raisin 580, 883
  rice 576, 878
  seed 574
  sorghum webworm 570, 861
  tobacco 579, 884
  wax 577, 868
  webbing clothes 566, 873, 1048
  white-shouldered house 561
Mouse, see Mice
Muddauber *599-600*, 948

Paper, see Damaged materials
Pill bugs(s) 7, 22
Pit viper 39
Pocket gopher(s) 78
Porcupine(s) 64
Pseudoscorpion(s) 7, 29
Psocid(s) 189, *264-273*, see book lice also
  common shiny winged 270
  cosmopolitan grain 271
  narrow winged house 273
  southern house 273
  spotted-winged grain 271
  vinegar barrel 272

Rabbit(s) 57, 59-63
Rat(s) *79-82*, 1010-1015, 1041-1042, 1071-
  1075
Rattle snake(s) 39, 40, 42
Roaches, see Cockroach
Rodent(s) 57, *59-82*, 1041-1042, 1054
Rub mark(s), see Secondary signs

Salamander(s) 34-35
Scorpion(s) 7, 27

vinegarroon 28
whip 7, 28
Secondary sign(s) 1, *1010-1075*, see
  Damaged materials also
  fecal pellets 1, 1011, 1035, *1059-1075*
  fecal stains 1, 1011, *1059-1075*
  foot prints 1013, *1072-1073*
  hairs 1, 1010, 1042, 1061, *1071-1075*
  rub marks 1014, *1072-1075*
  tooth marks 1, 1012, 1013, 1042, 1061,
    *1071-1075*
Shrew(s) 57-58
Silverfish 178, *206-208*, *1043-1044*, 1053,
  1064
Skunk(s) 54-56
Slug(s) 31, 32
Snail(s) 31, 32
Snake(s) 34, *36-43*
  copperhead 41
  coral 43
  non-poisonous 43
  pit viper 39
  rattlesnake 40, 42
  water moccasin 41
Snow flea(s) 200
Solpugids 29
Sowbug(s) 7, 21-22
Spider(s) 7, 23, 26, *155-168*
  black widow 167
  brown widow 168
  crab 164
  jumping 160
  red-legged widow 168
Springtail(s) 180, *199-200*
Squirrel(s) 66, *70-77*, 1010-1015, 1041-
  1042, *1071-1074*
  flying 66, 72-73
  ground 66, 70, 74
  tree 66, 74-77, 1073-1074

Tarantula(s) 155
Termite(s) 186-187, 198, *258-263*, *1019-
  1023*, 1030, 1070
Tick(s) 7, 23-25, *93-119*
  american dog 115, 117
  bat 95-98
  bird 96, 102-107
  brown dog 109
  brown winter 113
  cattle 109
  ear 98
  fowl 96
  guf coast 107
  hard 93, *104-119*
  lone star 107
  mammal 97, 98, 102-119
  pacific coast 114, 117
  rocky mountain wood 115, 119
  soft *93-103*
  spinose 98
  swallow 96

tropical horse 110
winter 113, 118
Toad(s) 34-35
Tooth mark(s), see Secondary signs
Treehopper(s) 196

Vertebrate(s) *33-82*
Vinegarroon 28
Viper(s) 39
Vole(s) 82, 1041

Wasp(s) 185, 198, 587, 588, *594-600*, 830-831, 836, 859, 947-951, 1034
social 588, *594-597*
solitary 588, 594, 599-600, 948-949, 1034
wood 1034
Water moccasin 41
Weevil(s) 194, 379, 383, 415, 434-435, 475-479, 480-484, 831, 859, 889, 893-895
bark 1017
bean 481, 484, 895
broadbean 484

broadnosed grain 476
coffee bean 519, 889
cowpea 481
granary 477, 889
lesser rice 478
long-horned 479
pea 481, 483, 894
rice 478, 889
seed 413, 481-484
snout 415, 434, 435, 475-479
southern cowpea 482, 895
strawberry root 479
wood 891-892, 1017
Whip scorpion(s) 7, 28
Wool chuck(s) 66-68
Wood pest(s) 258-263, 417-455, 592-593, 637-648, 1015-1042
Worm(s) 5, *8-20*
blood 982
hundred legged 5, *8-11*
thousand legged 5, *12-20*

Yellow jacket(s) 588, 595, 947